SO-BZZ-756

TREANOR'S ENGLISH SERIES

Exercises
in
English Grammar

BOOK II

JOHN H. TREANOR

Former Principal, Francis Parkman School, and
Director, Language Arts Curriculum Center, Boston

Educators Publishing Service, Inc.
Cambridge and Toronto

Educators Publishing Service, Inc.
31 Smith Place, Cambridge, Massachusetts 02138
1-800-225-5750

Copyright © 1992, 1972, 1963, 1958 by John H. Treanor. All rights reserved. No part of this book may be reproduced or utilized in any form or by any electronic or mechanical means, including photocopying, without permission in writing from the publisher. Printed in the U.S.A. ISBN 0-8388-0071-8

May 2000 Printing

TABLE OF CONTENTS

DEFINITIONS, WITH EXAMPLES, OF THE ITEMS COVERED IN EXERCISES IN ENGLISH GRAMMER, BOOK I

A SENTENCE expresses a complete thought. It begins with a capital letter and ends with a mark of punctuation.
Violent storms swept Texas.
Who answered the telephone?
The toast is burning!

A DECLARATIVE SENTENCE makes a statement.
Vacation begins tomorrow.

AN INTERROGATIVE SENTENCE asks a question.
Have you seen the morning paper?

AN IMPERATIVE SENTENCE orders something or gives a command.
Go home at once.

AN EXCLAMATORY SENTENCE shows strong feeling.
Call the police!

THE SUBJECT OF A SENTENCE is the part talked about.
The clock in the kitchen has stopped.

THE SIMPLE SUBJECT is the most important word in the subject.
The clock in the kitchen has stopped.

A COMPOUND SUBJECT contains two or more simple subjects.
A cowboy and his horse are resting in the shade.

THE PREDICATE OF A SENTENCE talks about the subject.
The oil from the well flamed for three weeks.

THE SIMPLE PREDICATE is the most important word in the predicate. It is always a verb.
The oil from the well <u>flamed</u> for three weeks.

A COMPOUND PREDICATE contains two or more simple predicates.
The flood <u>ruined the crops and washed away the soil.</u>

A NOUN is a word that names a person, place, or thing.
The <u>pendulum</u> of the <u>clock</u> swung in a slow <u>arc.</u>

A COMMON NOUN names a class of person, place, or thing.
Harry whistled for his <u>dog.</u>

A PROPER NOUN names a particular person, place, or thing. It always begins with a capital letter.
The dog paid no attention to <u>Harry.</u>

A COLLECTIVE NOUN is singular in form but plural in meaning.
A <u>clump</u> of lilacs stands by the fence.

AN ABSTRACT NOUN names a quality of something.
Jack's <u>kindness</u> pleased his mother.

A PREDICATE NOUN follows the verb and names the subject.
Today is <u>Sunday.</u>

A NOUN HAS NUMBER:
Singular: <u>mouse</u>   Plural: <u>mice</u>

A NOUN HAS GENDER:
Masculine: <u>boy</u>   Feminine: <u>girl</u>   Neuter: <u>house</u>

A PRONOUN takes the place of a noun.
<u>She</u> looked at <u>him.</u>

AN ADJECTIVE modifies a noun or a pronoun.
<u>Dark</u> shadows swept across the field.

A DESCRIPTIVE ADJECTIVE describes some quality of a noun.

A <u>heavy</u> explosion shattered the windows.

A LIMITING ADJECTIVE determines the number or quantity of a noun.

<u>Some</u> boys own <u>two</u> dogs.

A PREDICATE ADJECTIVE follows the verb and modifies the subject.

Apple pie tastes <u>good</u>.

A VERB is a word that shows action.
The bumblebee <u>buzzed</u> against the window.

A VERB PHRASE contains more than one word.
The children <u>had been swimming</u> in the pond.

AN AUXILIARY VERB helps the principal verb.
The children <u>had been</u> swimming in the pond.

A LINKING VERB joins parts of the sentence.

The money <u>is</u> in the top drawer.
The runner <u>grew</u> tired.

A VERB IS IN THE ACTIVE VOICE when its subject does something.

The snake <u>slithers</u> through the tall grass.

A VERB IS IN THE PASSIVE VOICE when its subject has something done to it.

The wheat <u>was harvested</u> by the farmers.

AN ADVERB modifies a verb, an adjective, or another adverb.

The colonists settled <u>finally</u> at Plymouth.

Today seems <u>rather</u> cold.

He spoke <u>too</u> quickly.

AN ADVERB OF MANNER answers the question <u>how</u> or <u>in what manner</u>.

The swimmer plunged <u>deeply</u> into the pool.

AN ADVERB OF TIME answers the question <u>when</u> or <u>how often</u>.

<u>Sometimes</u> it snows in the summer.

AN ADVERB OF PLACE answers the question <u>where</u>.
We searched <u>everywhere</u> for the money.

A PREPOSITION introduces a phrase.
The cat disappeared <u>into</u> the darkness.

A CONJUNCTION joins words or groups of words.
March <u>and</u> April are rainy months.

AN INTERJECTION is a word used to express feeling.
<u>Oh</u>, what a beautiful garden.

A TRANSITIVE VERB requires a direct object to complete its meaning.

I <u>bought</u> a ten-speed bicycle.

A DIRECT OBJECT is the word or group of words that completes the meaning of a transitive verb.

I bought a ten-speed <u>bicycle</u>.

AN INTRANSITIVE VERB does not require a direct object.

The telephone <u>rang</u> for ten minutes.

AN INDIRECT OBJECT denotes to whom or to which
something is given.

The druggist handed <u>the woman</u> the medicine.

A PHRASE is a group of related words without subject
or predicate.
<u>near the swampy meadow</u>

AN ADJECTIVE PHRASE modifies a noun.
the dog <u>with a bushy tail</u>

AN ADVERBIAL PHRASE modifies a verb.
John came home <u>from Germany</u>.

A CLAUSE is a group of related words with a subject
and a predicate.

<u>A rainbow brightened the sky.</u>
<u>although the dog barked</u>

A PRINCIPAL CLAUSE makes complete sense. It is
always a sentence.

<u>Two jet airplanes whizzed through the clouds</u>.

A SUBORDINATE CLAUSE does not make complete sense.
It is not a sentence.
<u>unless the rain stops before noon</u>

A SIMPLE SENTENCE has one principal clause.
<u>The ladder leans against the barn</u>.

A COMPOUND SENTENCE has at least two principal
clauses.
<u>The snow has stopped, but the wind continues</u>
<u>to blow</u>.

A COMPLEX SENTENCE has one principal clause and
at least one subordinate clause.
<u>Since the apples are ripe, we should pick them</u>.

Exercises in English Grammar, Book II presupposes a knowledge of basic grammar. Should further study of the preceding items be needed, the pupil is urged to review the drill material in *Exercises in English Grammar, Book I.*

NOUN — NOMINATIVE CASE

> The case of a noun depends upon its use. When a noun is used as subject of a sentence, it is in the nominative case.

Nouns underlined are in the nominative case:

1. The <u>library</u> should be open every morning.
2. Straining every muscle, the <u>batter</u> aimed at the ball.
3. The little <u>boy</u> gazed anxiously at the doctor's face.
4. Not far beyond the bridge lay the <u>scene</u> of our joy.
5. The mournful <u>wind</u> blew across the desolate island.

Find the nouns in the nominative case:

1. An odd expression came over his face.
2. Here comes the mail carrier down the street.
3. During the long, silent night came the tick of the clock.
4. The energetic teenagers raced down the court.
5. We finally won the hard-fought game.
6. She sprained her ankle skiing.
7. At camp last summer Richard won a swimming medal.
8. The graduates filed slowly to the platform.
9. A cloud of steam rose from the boiling pot.

10. The tires on my uncle's car are not very good.

11. A load of gravel ought to be dumped in the hole.

12. Suddenly a distant but unmistakable shot rang out.

13. The heat and the fleas made the puppy very irritable.

14. The wind seemed to rise with the setting sun.

15. A long drawn-out whistle disclosed the train's approach.

16. The huge steel bridge arched across the wide river.

17. The results of our poll revealed many surprises.

18. Not everyone knows how to change a tire.

19. He struggled with the storm windows.

20. Will you please hand me that book?

21. September is the month of hurricanes in North America.

Use these nouns in the nominative case:

1. catalogue	6. circus	11. aunt	16. victory
2. spring	7. printing press	12. tiger	17. herd
3. garden	8. courage	13. swamp	18. uniform
4. fleet	9. meadow	14. anxiety	19. film
5. twilight	10. Henry	15. sword	20. industry

NOUN — POSSESSIVE CASE

The case of a noun depends upon its use. When a noun is used to show ownership, it is in the possessive case.

Nouns underlined are in the possessive case:

1. With hesitation he rang the <u>doctor's</u> bell.
2. In this store we sell <u>women's</u> clothing.
3. The <u>neighbor's</u> dog annoys us by barking.
4. <u>Pupils'</u> tickets are on sale every Monday.
5. Follow the <u>librarian's</u> suggestion.

Find the nouns in the possessive case:

1. The children laughed at the clown's funny face.
2. Boys and girls should pay attention to their parents' advice.
3. In the bird's nest lay three sky-blue eggs.
4. We enjoyed the quartet's recital.
5. My friend's problems become my own.
6. The organist's fingers were poised above the keys.
7. He found the author's meaning quite obscure.
8. The team's uniforms are black and orange.
9. The sun's rays penetrated the thick foliage.

Use these nouns in the possessive case:

1. teacher	18. pianist	35. navigator
2. Elizabeth	19. cow	36. pharmacist
3. mail carrier	20. American	37. chauffeur
4. duck	21. hairdresser	38. storm
5. Alberta	22. athlete	39. councils
6. elephant	23. David	40. team
7. miner	24. Wyoming	41. sister
8. city	25. Ms. Allison	42. governor
9. tramp	26. painter	43. tiger
10. messenger	27. dentist	44. conductor
11. birds	28. visitor	45. baker
12. principal	29. president	46. Madeline
13. country	30. animal	47. Arthur
14. farmer	31. child	48. pilot
15. operator	32. bankers	49. bee
16. sailor	33. plumber	50. coach
17. stenographer	34. grocer	51. soldier

NOUN — SINGULAR POSSESSIVE

When a noun expresses ownership it is in the possessive case. Possessives may be singular or plural.

The singular possessives are underlined:

1. The <u>Korean's</u> speech was very fluent.
2. The <u>woman's</u> fear was appropriate.
3. A <u>child's</u> appetite is often insatiable.
4. The <u>carpenter's</u> bill came in <u>today's</u> mail.
5. We ran quickly when we heard the <u>child's</u> cry.

Find the singular possessives:

1. The dog's tricks are amusing to its owners.
2. The doctor's work was not finished.
3. Dr. Martin Luther King, Jr.'s life is an inspiration to many.
4. We raised the ship's sail with difficulty.
5. Is a rattlesnake's bite always fatal?
6. The cashier's check is your receipt.
7. That restaurant's pizzas are the best in town.
8. A turkey's eggs are larger than a duck's eggs.

Use these nouns as singular possessives:

1. Mr. Andrews	18. storm	35. elephant
2. school	19. skeleton	36. child
3. town	20. muskrat	37. ox
4. motorcycle	21. policeman	38. goose
5. sailor	22. player	39. car
6. teacher	23. doctor	40. woman
7. Ms. Holiday	24. sheep	41. ship
8. Kevin	25. morning	42. vacation
9. horse	26. mountain	43. thunder
10. computer	27. boat	44. tire
11. country	28. mother	45. druggist
12. conqueror	29. soldier	46. skateboard
13. trumpet	30. music	47. bell
14. fire engine	31. bicycle	48. train
15. whistle	32. Seattle	49. house
16. auditorium	33. deep	50. hour
17. submarine	34. year	51. aunt

NOUN — PLURAL POSSESSIVE

> When a noun expresses ownership it is in the
> possessive case. Possessives may be singular or plural.

The plural possessives are underlined:

1. The <u>bankers'</u> conference closed today.
2. <u>Lawyers'</u> actions must also be legal.
3. The <u>firemen's</u> best efforts did not save the house.
4. She dried both <u>turkeys'</u> wishbones.
5. Many <u>athletes'</u> trophies are now on display.

Find the plural possessives:

1. Most colleges require four years' study.
2. The cars' fenders intertwined.
3. Motorcyclists' licenses may be obtained after school.
4. Children's drawings are often colorful and bold.
5. Ducks' feathers make soft pillows.
6. We had to remember all of the characters' names.
7. He ignored his friends' entreaties.

Use these nouns in the plural possessive form:

1. nation	18. companion	35. pilot
2. bird	19. soldier	36. servant
3. man	20. waiter	37. policeman
4. child	21. chauffeur	38. monkey
5. flower	22. donkey	39. city
6. skate	23. mariner	40. thief
7. gardener	24. craftsman	41. operator
8. horse	25. ruler	42. messenger
9. town	26. nurse	43. king
10. dictator	27. instructor	44. ostrich
11. diplomat	28. pelican	45. church
12. tutor	29. hound	46. grandmother
13. parent	30. brother	47. veteran
14. elm	31. classmate	48. clown
15. penguin	32. swimmer	49. ancestor
16. acrobat	33. counterfeiter	50. wolf
17. fish	34. pioneer	51. traveler

NOUN — OBJECTIVE CASE

> The case of a noun depends upon its use. When a noun is used as the object of a transitive verb, it is in the objective case.

Nouns underlined are in the objective case:

1. Quite accidentally, the boys broke the <u>window.</u>
2. The baby fell and cut her <u>mouth.</u>
3. These library books have leather <u>bindings.</u>
4. Every Sunday I enjoy symphonic <u>music.</u>
5. The rain deluged the <u>earth.</u>

Find the nouns in the objective case, object of the verb:

1. A busy camper was sewing his moccasins.
2. Will you meet the train at ten o'clock?
3. The wind scatters all these papers.
4. The children carefully polished their shoes.
5. The mail carrier just left two letters for you.
6. The proud parents exhibited their twins.
7. An October moon illuminated the entire valley.
8. When he lost the prize, chagrin filled his heart.
9. The bare trees are casting long, dark shadows.

Use these nouns in the objective case, as the objects of verbs:

1. piano	18. whistle	35. office
2. autumn	19. dexterity	36. squadron
3. sky	20. tiger	37. anxiety
4. courage	21. calendar	38. bicycle
5. blizzard	22. pen	39. often
6. hammer	23. fountain	40. traffic
7. tree	24. clarinet	41. timidity
8. success	25. glacier	42. toys
9. broadcast	26. winter	43. New Hampshire
10. desk	27. dictionary	44. anticipation
11. flagpole	28. love	45. tools
12. locomotive	29. examination	46. ancestors
13. kindness	30. sagacity	47. companions
14. circle	31. accident	48. exercise
15. subway	32. industry	49. conflagration
16. twilight	33. curtains	50. appetite
17. garage	34. maze	51. stroll

NOUN AS OBJECT OF PREPOSITION

> The case of a noun depends upon its use. When a noun is used as the object of a preposition, it is in the objective case.

The object of the preposition is underlined:

1. Not within my <u>memory</u> has such a storm occurred.
2. All law should be based upon equal <u>justice</u>.
3. Throughout the <u>night</u> the wind howled.
4. I have not been home since this <u>morning</u>.
5. The little red fox scampered over the <u>hill</u>.

Find the noun as object of a preposition:

1. None of my books has been returned.
2. Sitting by the brook, the fisherman gazed at his line.
3. The hikers gathered some grapes along the roadside.
4. All but the fat, white duck complained at the storm.
5. The tall elm stood erect against the gray sky.
6. After our home lessons, we usually go for a walk.
7. The red signal appeared beyond the railway station.
8. A flock of geese settled on the pond near the island.
9. With a sigh, she slipped the key into the lock.

10. All except three students passed the test.

11. Filled with curiosity, the children walked through the zoo.

12. Down the street marched many striking workers.

13. The telephone on the table rang with a loud noise.

14. Play near the shore but keep in sight.

15. Such actions are entirely unlike Tom.

16. Without fail, we must be home at six o'clock.

17. She was invited to see the movie on her neighbor's VCR.

18. The sailor kept struggling until the rescue.

Use these nouns as objects of a preposition:

1. compass	9. canoe	17. whale
2. submarine	10. library	18. electrician
3. violin	11. bulb	19. history
4. searchlight	12. magazine	20. mechanic
5. freedom	13. possession	21. clock
6. barometer	14. eraser	22. bear
7. solitude	15. employment	23. wheel
8. operation	16. sympathy	24. power

NOUN AS APPOSITIVE

A noun following another noun to explain or identify it is called an appositive. An appositive with its modifiers is usually enclosed by commas.

The appositive is underlined:

1. Most of the kids stood on the corner, the <u>place</u> to hang out.
2. His daughter, <u>Allison</u>, is a real ornithologist.
3. Augusta, Maine, the <u>capital</u> of the state, is on the Kennebec.
4. Even when Beethoven, the <u>composer</u>, became deaf, he continued to write music.
5. The shed, John's <u>workshop</u>, is being painted.

Find the appositives:

1. The rising wind, a piercing howl, gave us shivers.
2. Robert Frost, a twentieth-century poet, lived in New England.
3. Sally examined her broken bicycle, her only transportation.
4. The electric train, a welcome toy, occupied his time.
5. The race horses, graceful aristocrats, waited nervously at the starting gate.
6. The rain, a deluge of long duration, made the river rise.
7. Tommy clutched the silver watch, his grandfather's gift.
8. Mr. Anderson, my neighbor, raised organic tomatoes.

9. They said I could play their piano, an instrument always perfectly tuned.

10. The refugees returned to the valley, their land before the war.

11. The clock, a mahogany timepiece, was very old.

12. When it appeared she could wait no longer, we told the visitor, a nervous woman, to go in.

13. The bell, signal to leave, echoed in the corridors.

14. Philadelphia, city of brotherly love, has grown to great size.

15. Using a blanket he smothered the blazing oil, source of the fire.

16. For the first time I have just met him, her nephew.

17. The flag, symbol of the country, flapped on the pole.

18. Native Americans once traveled on the woodland streams, roadways for an entire region.

19. Use Route 109, the shortest way to Pittsfield.

20. How he hated the drug, source of all his troubles.

21. At last came the low whistle, the signal they were awaiting.

22. Receive this medal, badge of highest honor.

23. You have to invite our cousins, Michael, Joanne, and Sara.

24. Allan, the librarian's brother, is dead.

25. This book belongs to Ms. Smith, the principal.

26. We praised Jennifer, the girl who brings the paper.

NOMINATIVE OF ADDRESS

A noun used in direct address
is in the nominative case.

The nouns in direct address are underlined:

1. <u>Karen</u>, you pitch next inning.
2. Look, <u>Uncle Tom</u>, I just caught a trout.
3. Hey <u>you</u>, get out of the way!
4. <u>Sam</u>, can you make bread?
5. If I knew, <u>Jennifer</u>, I would tell you.

Find the nouns in direct address in the nominative case:

1. Folks, the office is now open for you to buy your tickets.
2. Ladies and gentlemen, I welcome you this evening to our concert.
3. Look, my friends, it's pretty late.
4. All right, Carl, I'll meet you at the corner.
5. Did you hear that loud explosion, Stephanie?
6. Friends and neighbors, cast your votes for Smiggins.
7. Get down, Rover, get down!
8. Now, boys, can't you be a little quieter?
9. Yes, Jean, I finished putting that into the computer.
10. Fellow Americans, today we celebrate the end of the war.

11. Well, Judge, I think the trial was fair.

12. Can you come to see the baby, Doctor Kernan?

13. Say, kids, would you mind sitting still?

14. Officer, arrest that man!

15. Hey, lifeguard, we need help over here!

16. Now, friends and relatives, be seated.

17. Sir, are you looking for something?

18. In a moment, Joe, I'll have the motor fixed.

19. Have you any extra money, Ellen?

20. If I had a pen, Larry, I would sign these letters.

21. Oh, Aunt Mary, thank you for the pretty sweater!

22. Just be patient, Hans!

23. Please, Ben, sharpen this chisel.

Use these nouns in sentences as nominatives of address:

1. Martha	4. Uncle Ed	7. folks
2. fellow citizens	5. Doctor Cass	8. Mike
3. Miss Turley	6. boys and girls	9. neighbor

NOUN REVIEW

In the following sentences, find and identify the various kinds of nouns:

1. In the fall we enjoy football and soccer.

2. Michelle, show the visitor the way to the principal's office.

3. Chopin, the composer, died at an early age.

4. The woman and man who live next door are both architects.

5. A swarm of black flies caused the hiker's irritation.

6. To make and fly a kite successfully requires skill and creativity.

7. Truman was President of the United States.

8. Massachusetts has often produced great inventors.

9. The sudden wind scattered the neighbors' papers.

10. With the keenest attention, he heard his father's plan.

11. Sharpen these pencils with your new knife.

12. The doctor handled the instruments with dexterity.

13. The orchestra is the Boston Symphony.

14. In the autumn in Ontario we think of red and yellow leaves.

15. A cluster of yellow dandelions tossed in the breeze.

16. The teenagers spent a day making a long toboggan.

17. Latin and mathematics require hours of study.

18. We hope for the day when all peoples' liberties will be restored.

19. The sculptor showed John a beautiful statue.

20. A memorial to Vietnam soldiers was erected in Washington.

21. A shower of glass fell suddenly from the car window.

22. The storm disappeared and the sun came out.

23. Donald, the paper boy, has been early this week.

24. Thick clouds of pungent smoke obscured the sun.

25. The train rushed along the beautiful Connecticut shore.

26. A tremendous sense of relief filled her heart.

27. With great energy, a colony of ants labored on their hill.

28. Traffic along the highway increases on Sundays.

29. Show this note to your mother or father.

30. He measured the window frame and set the glass.

31. Let me express to you my deepest sympathy.

32. The visitor is your old friend from Arizona.

33. A roar of applause marked the winning touchdown.

34. All of us spent Saturday putting on storm windows.

PERSONAL PRONOUN

> Personal pronouns denote the speaker (first person), the person spoken to (second person), or the person or thing spoken of (third person).

The personal pronouns are underlined:

First person:
1. <u>I</u> succeeded in my endeavor.
2. <u>We</u> ought to be more careful.
3. Give <u>me</u> five more minutes.

Second person:
1. <u>You</u> may sit in that chair.
2. <u>You</u> make a fine team.
3. Is this harmonica <u>yours</u>?

Third person:
1. <u>He</u> gave <u>them</u> final instructions.
2. <u>She</u> had not seen <u>him</u> in the yard.
3. I claim this ball as <u>his.</u>
4. <u>They</u> challenged the victors.

Find the personal pronouns:

1. I think the work is too difficult for you.
2. It sat on the doorstep and barked at us.
3. This mathematics paper is certainly hers.
4. Come here to me and I will help you.

5. You ought to see the stamp exhibit at the library.

6. The drawing instruments belong to me.

7. He and I have been friends for many years.

8. It thrust a venomous tongue at us.

9. We cannot afford to paint the house just now.

10. She gave us the most delicious picnic I can remember.

11. Mother saw them stealing the grapes from the vine.

12. Football is evidently too strenuous for you.

13. They spoke very highly of John's ability.

14. He brought it to the cobbler's to be repaired.

15. The journey was a wild experience for us.

16. Let go of the sail or we shall capsize!

17. The captain watched them disappear into the woods.

18. The low, white house near the lake is ours.

19. We might have invited them to the party.

20. You give us too little time for the examination.

21. He might have warned them and us, too.

PERSONAL PRONOUN - NOMINATIVE CASE

> A personal pronoun used as subject of a sentence
> is in the nominative case.

Pronouns underlined are in the nominative case:

1. <u>We</u> have little time and less opportunity.
2. Presently <u>I</u> propose to telephone your home.
3. <u>They</u> enjoy moderate but ample exercise.
4. Have <u>you</u> listened to the news tonight?
5. <u>She</u> cannot have understood the question.

Find the pronouns in the nominative case:

1. Somehow he achieved the desired prize.
2. It whined and held up an injured paw.
3. They negotiated a settlement of the strike.
4. We all enjoyed several fine films.
5. Have I understood your perplexity?
6. Has he signified his intention of replying?
7. We have often admired your tenacity.
8. Not yet do I concede your victory.
9. By taking evening courses, she acquired new skills.

10. Would he exhaust the teacher's patience?

11. They suggested an alternate route to town.

12. You might have pursued a vigorous course.

13. I was outraged by the continual insults.

14. Have we not met before?

15. He underestimated the opponent's strength.

16. Yesterday she revised the blueprint.

17. I could just barely make out a figure in the thick fog.

18. Why don't you try a new method as an experiment?

19. Yesterday they auctioned all possessions.

20. We endeavored to meet the author.

21. I seem to have made a serious blunder.

22. It burned to the ground in half an hour.

23. He and I were affectionate companions.

24. Of course you will earn a diploma.

25. She answered in a cultivated voice.

26. They uttered an impetuous shout of joy.

27. Formerly we lived in a desolate spot.

PERSONAL PRONOUN — POSSESSIVE CASE

> A personal pronoun used to show ownership is in the possessive case. When the pronoun is used as an adjective, it is called a pronominal adjective.

Pronouns in the possessive case and pronominal adjectives are underlined:

1. <u>Our</u> contribution to the scholarship fund has been received.
2. <u>Your</u> bicycle is different from <u>theirs</u>.
3. Here come <u>your</u> friends and <u>mine</u>.
4. <u>His</u> story highly amused the assembly.
5. <u>Our</u> next birthday party will be <u>hers</u>.

Find the pronouns in the possessive case:

1. My opinion had been frequently asked.
2. Dramatic ability is his one claim to distinction.
3. Their historic house attracts throngs of visitors.
4. Her grandmother has invited her to the summer cottage.
5. Your last composition is by far the best.
6. Have the council members even heard of our plan?
7. Such honors as theirs come only from hard work.
8. My description of the accident is not entirely clear.
9. Having broken his pen, John asked for mine.

10. My oldest friend recently died in Cleveland.

11. Is Alice sure that the wallet is hers?

12. The elephant lifted its huge trunk into the air.

13. Her graceful performance delighted the audience.

14. I doubt if the pocketbook and watch are ours.

15. Two copies of the <u>National Geographic Magazine</u> are his.

16. By request, she sang her song again.

17. Two pupils have not taken your exam.

18. Let all competitors come forward with their model buildings.

19. Any dog will fight for its bone.

20. Ours is the last white house on the street.

21. It is not difficult to locate their farm.

22. Father has not seen her report card.

23. Your answer to the problem is exactly right.

24. Either John's bicycle or mine has a flat tire.

25. A new radio was delivered to our house.

26. His response to the appeal is most gratifying.

27. The ticket is yours for the asking.

PERSONAL PRONOUN — OBJECTIVE CASE

A personal pronoun used as object of a verb or as object of a preposition is in the objective case.

Pronouns in the objective case are underlined:

1. Mathematics generally perplexes me.
2. A pair of racing skates was given to him.
3. Peering through the fog for the wharf, I finally see it.
4. To you the entire school owes great thanks.
5. Wait near the corner for me.

Find the pronouns in the objective case:

1. At first the French student could not understand me.
2. The neighbors could not believe her.
3. Just as the storm broke, the farmer noticed it.
4. To them, as to all brave rescue workers, the community gives thanks.
5. A crowd watched them playing tennis.
6. Father has often taken us to see the ice show.
7. Did the dentist give you another appointment?
8. The mechanic found the wire and examined it.
9. The policewoman spoke to me after the accident.

10. The teacher noticed them near the lockers.

11. Carry these heavy books for her.

12. Place the map near you.

13. Father never was known to speak of it afterwards.

14. A bolt of lightning split them down the center.

15. The clean-up captain handed a garbage bag to me.

16. Friends have sometimes seen her at the museum.

17. Rick puzzles us more and more.

18. The dog often barked at him and the monkey.

19. To see the coast of Baja California is indeed to like it.

20. The explosion alarmed us very much.

21. The teachers are glad to recommend her.

22. The navigator took the bearings and jotted them down.

23. A whirring car alarm aroused us last night.

24. The last problem is for you to do.

25. Has anyone seen them near the playground?

26. Will the boys remind him of Saturday's game?

27. Everyone noticed it on her wrist.

28. Will the teacher give another chance to them?

DEMONSTRATIVE PRONOUN

> A demonstrative pronoun
> points out a person or thing.

The demonstrative pronouns are underlined:

1. <u>This</u> is my first attempt at writing verse.
2. <u>Those</u> appear to be very good apples.
3. Would you like to read <u>these</u>?
4. <u>That</u> is our house at the end of the street.

Using demonstrative pronouns (this, that, these, those)
make sentences including these words.

1. a cold night	11. sudden storms	21. bright gold
2. sour pickles	12. black cat	22. my friends
3. broken wheel	13. lighted pumpkins	23. party gifts
4. new bicycle	14. forbidden paths	24. your lessons
5. strange person	15. happy days	25. your reward
6. odd sounds	16. my ice skates	26. pretty dress
7. new report	17. brilliant stars	27. swift birds
8. bad conduct	18. new automobile	28. high prices
9. high wind	19. handsome man	29. old books
10. summer camp	20. old eraser	30. my purse

INTERROGATIVE PRONOUN

> An interrogative pronoun
> is used in asking a question.

The interrogative pronouns are underlined:

1. <u>Who</u> has finished his work?
2. <u>Whom</u> has the principal interviewed?
3. <u>Whose</u> will be the best paper?
4. <u>What</u> is the nature of his illness?

Using interrogative pronouns (who, whom, what, whose, which), make sentences including these words.

1.	brown dog	11.	funny animal	21.	of the girls
2.	fix the clock	12.	dust the room	22.	on the phone
3.	of my books	13.	called me	23.	baseball glove
4.	latest program	14.	of his poems	24.	of their trees
5.	red scarf	15.	the parade	25.	tell me
6.	the noisy party	16.	report card	26.	tonight's show
7.	your father	17.	of the apples	27.	the puppy
8.	this hat	18.	for Thanksgiving	28.	of her stories
9.	of our pupils	19.	the noise	29.	to the store
10.	bake a cake	20.	sudden cry	30.	had he seen

INDEFINITE PRONOUN

An indefinite pronoun
refers to an indefinite person or thing.

These are the usual indefinite pronouns:

another	each	one
another's	either	one's
any	neither	other
both	none	some

Find the indefinite pronouns in these sentences:

1. Another's will not satisfy your teacher.

2. Any who are energetic may come on the hike.

3. Each must do his own work.

4. Others may try this example.

5. Some do not appear to be listening.

6. Success depends upon one's ability.

7. Would you like to follow another's advice?

8. Today I have not heard from either of the men.

9. None of the plays in the game were new.

10. Some have received a very low mark.

11. If you are good, you may have another.

12. The prisoner had heard by mail from neither.

13. The grocer cannot give you any today.

14. Won't you give me some?

15. Not one has remembered to give thanks.

16. There are enough boats for each to go rowing.

17. With another, would the mechanic do better?

18. At holiday time, presents are given to each.

19. Both of the children are quite sick.

20. Another's has been chosen for the exhibition.

21. Others must follow this regulation as well as you.

22. Some of the leaves have already fallen.

23. Any who prefer it may have chocolate.

24. Either will be satisfactory to use.

25. The weather often interferes with one's plans.

26. If this knife is dull, is there another?

27. Won't you give me this one?

28. Neither of you has done his best.

29. None of the answers is correct.

RELATIVE PRONOUN — ANTECEDENT

> A relative pronoun relates a subordinate clause to a noun or pronoun in a principal clause. The noun or the pronoun is then called an antecedent.

The relative pronoun and its antecedent are underlined:

1. The <u>players</u> <u>who</u> won the championship received gold medals.
2. The <u>building</u>, <u>which</u> burned last night, was an old landmark.
3. The <u>man</u> to <u>whom</u> I spoke is Doctor Manning.
4. <u>Pupils</u> <u>whose</u> notebooks are completed may go home.
5. The <u>swimmer</u> <u>that</u> shouted needs help!

Find the relative pronoun and its antecedent:

1. Food that is nourishing usually tastes good.
2. The lesson that he assigned will take an hour.
3. The lawyer, whose words were impressive, easily won the case.
4. Billy met the man who owned the motorcycle.
5. The neighbor whom I had avoided proved to be friendly.
6. The man for whom I work is Mr. Gordon.

Note to teachers: Nonrestrictive clauses are set off with commas.

IVE PRONOUN — POSSESSIVE CASE

> pronoun in the possessive case relates
> in the subordinate clause to the antecedent
> ence.

ronoun in the possessive case and its ante-
derlined:

rmer <u>whose</u> collie dog was struck by a
very upset.

ctionary, to <u>whose</u> pages I turned, gave
rect spelling.

d, for <u>whose</u> father I work, is my oldest

lady, <u>whose</u> yard I usually mow, often feeds
okies.

ple-decker <u>house</u>, <u>whose</u> owners had aban-
it, was renovated by the neighborhood.

ve pronoun in the possessive case and its

ook, whose cover is torn, goes at half-price.

we drove into the tunnel, whose darkness
penetrable, we were afraid.

owalski, to whose boy I gave the bicycle,
ost grateful.

tomobile whose motor is burning oil
new piston rings.

7. The story, whose ending was fantastic, seemed incredible.

8. Gossip, which is often harmful, should be discouraged.

9. The family, which moved to Oregon, has returned.

10. The man who rang the doorbell had a telegram in his hand.

11. The noise that Terry heard awoke her mother, too.

12. The baby, whose arms are covered with a rash, should be in bed.

13. Ask the pupil who sits near you.

14. Miss Marshall, by whom I was taught, has just retired.

15. The boat, which is anchored near the dock, should be hauled ashore.

16. My daughter, for whom you inquired, now works in Chicago.

17. Men that are strong can perform heavy tasks.

18. Any flag whose colors are faded should be replaced.

19. The day, whose heat was oppressive, was most uncomfortable.

20. The company to which Andrea applied for work had no openings.

RELATIVE PRONOUN — NOMINATIVE CASE

> A relative pronoun used as the subject of a subordinate clause is in the nominative case.

The relative pronoun and its antecedent are underlined:

1. The <u>child</u> <u>who</u> ate the green apples became ill.
2. The <u>woman</u> <u>who</u> owns the store gave me a candy bar.
3. <u>Pupils</u> <u>who</u> study faithfully usually succeed.
4. The <u>sergeant,</u> <u>who</u> was peering through the field glasses, saw a moving shadow.
5. The <u>landlord,</u> <u>who</u> entered the building, demanded his rent.

Find the relative pronoun in the nominative case; find also its antecedent:

1. Alice has the music that arrived last week.
2. A storm, which erupted suddenly, wrecked the fishing trawler.
3. This is the outfielder who broke his wrist.
4. All who knew the artist admired her skill.
5. No one remained alive who remembered the old mill.
6. Is it you who smashed this bottle?
7. Take this package to the store that is next to the post office.
8. The mountain road, which was narrow and winding, was passable.

42

9. The boy who won firs[t] principal.
10. Parents who work ha[rd] their children.
11. The laws, which regu[late] constantly monitore[d]
12. Teachers often prais[e] couragement.
13. Melanie has a new d[ress]
14. The two firemen wh[o] were injured.
15. Anne, who was acce[pted] choice, thinks she is lives.
16. The scarf, which is [torn]
17. This is the girl who
18. Is it you who wrote
19. All who know him
20. He now has the bo[ok]
21. The children who [ran] down.
22. My typewriter, wh[ich]
23. The tree that is in
24. The highways, wh[ich] new, need repairs

RE[LATIVE]

> A rela[tive]
> owner[ship]
> in the [...]

The relativ[e ...]
cedent are [...]

1. Th[e] car[...]
2. The the [...]
3. Ed[ward] frie[nd]
4. An[...] me [...]
5. The don[...]

Find the rel[ative]
antecedent:

1. That
2. Whe[n] was [...]
3. Mrs. was [...]
4. Any [...] need[s]

5. The Adirondacks attract many campers, whose choices of campsites are numerous.

6. Pike's Peak, whose summit is covered with snow, can be seen for fifty miles.

7. Patricia, whose watch is broken, cannot be expected to arrive on time.

8. The boy whose leg was broken in two places had an operation.

9. The tumultuous storm, whose wind was of hurricane force, blew down an apple orchard.

10. August, whose days seemed endless, is almost over.

11. Our burns came from the sun, whose rays were too strong.

12. We learned too late that the daycare center whose services we needed was closing.

13. We always hurry past our neighbor's dog, whose bark is threatening.

14. Janet, whose coat sleeve was torn, mended it in two minutes.

RELATIVE PRONOUN — OBJECTIVE CASE

> A relative pronoun used as object of a
> verb or of a preposition is in the objective case.

The relative pronoun in the objective case and its antecedent
are underlined:

1. The <u>director</u> with <u>whom</u> I interviewed hired me as
   nature counselor.
2. The <u>road</u> by <u>which</u> we reached Stockbridge has
   been resurfaced.
3. The <u>violinist</u>, to <u>whom</u> we directed our applause,
   played two encores.
4. His <u>mother</u>, for <u>whom</u> he bought the new lamp,
   was greatly astonished.
5. The <u>principal</u>, from <u>whom</u> the pupils received
   their diplomas, praised the boys and girls.

Find the relative pronoun in the objective case; also
find its antecedent:

1. Employers for whom we work should keep us
   informed of hazardous working conditions.
2. The post office, to which I hurried, had just
   been closed.
3. The subway train by which we traveled was
   crowded.
4. The pupil to whom our teacher had spoken
   was disorderly again.

5. The loudmouthed kid, whom we tried to avoid, was standing on the corner.

6. The mail carrier, for whom we sometimes watch, is again late.

7. We can hire four of the teenagers from whom you took applications.

8. The saxophone, on which John practiced every day, was what he loved most.

9. We worked to reduce the use of fluorocarbons, by which the ozone is destroyed.

10. The bank president, whom everyone trusted, embezzled the money.

11. The college from which I received the acceptance letter is not my first choice.

12. At the first trial, the plan which we devised succeeded.

13. The box into which I flung the hammer was full of other tools.

14. The politician, whom we do not trust, almost won the election.

NUMBER, GENDER, AND CASE OF RELATIVE PRONOUNS

A relative pronoun has the same number and gender as its antecedent, but takes its case from its use in the subordinate or relative clause.

Find the number, the gender, and the case of the following relative pronouns:

1. The principles by which we live should be thought about carefully.

2. The actress, about whom you speak, once lived in Florida.

3. Both passengers, who had been injured, were taken to the emergency room.

4. The car for which I bargained was in fine condition.

5. The light on the dashboard, by which we could read the speedometer, went out.

6. Although I hurried, the students for whom I was looking had already left the library.

7. This rule to which I refer has no exceptions.

8. The train that approaches is from Chicago.

9. The bicycle store, whose remodeling is finished, invites the public to an open house.

10. The drug case about which the reporter was writing would be the next one to be tried.

11. I telephoned the plumber, who will be here soon.

12. The taxidriver, to whom the doorman called, apparently did not hear him.

13. The garage, which was quite old, caught fire one night.

14. The restaurant, whose dinners are famous, is filled every night.

15. Indira Gandhi is the leader about whom we are to study.

16. An understanding of geometry, which is studied in high school, can be very useful in engineering.

17. Five little children, who are all cousins, are having a party.

18. The tire that blew out failed us at the wrong time.

19. The judge, to whom the prisoner appealed, could not relent.

20. The articles about which I spoke are in this set of books.

21. The fence which our neighbor is repairing fell down in the storm.

22. Those who do not pass the test must take it again.

23. Malnutrition, from which many children die, can be eliminated.

24. Who knows best does not always act best.

25. Diseases like cancer and Alzheimer's, whose causes are not known, can be very frightening.

PRONOUN REVIEW

In the following sentences find the pronouns and tell how they are used:

1. Each is required to make his own way.

2. That train going by is the Merchants' Limited.

3. Your grapes are even better than I had supposed.

4. The bell that we hear is on a buoy in the harbor.

5. The man to whom we appealed agreed to help us.

6. All pupils whose work is done are permitted to go.

7. Any who wish to pass the test ought to review this chapter.

8. Whose are these high-top sneakers lying on the floor?

9. This notice is addressed to all who read it.

10. Would you like to see our garden?

11. This boy, whom I do not even know, has broken my car window.

12. Do you think Mother will be able to find another?

13. The path, by which they descended the mountain, was very steep.

14. The musicians, whom we applauded, broke into an encore.

15. The doctor about whom he inquired could not be located.

16. These do not seem to be good apples.

17. Nations whose policies are predatory are usually eventually defeated.

18. He drove off the dog that was chasing the squirrel.

19. She gave us a bad fright when she fell.

20. The movie video, which we watched, was not very interesting.

21. The concert to which we went was packed with enthusiastic fans.

22. We waved to the train that was passing by.

23. Some of this candy is homemade.

24. The carpenter to whom we spoke is coming tomorrow.

25. The chicken which she bought must have been very old.

26. We nodded to the neighbors whom we had just passed.

27. Who broke the apartment window?

28. The job for which he applied has gone to another.

29. People who live in glass houses should not throw stones.

30. The apples which they picked were early Baldwins.

31. Send John to the drugstore for another.

32. The striking workers to whom he spoke appeared quite upset.

33. The sun, which had been very hot, was now obscured by clouds.

34. Here is the window that your son has broken.

35. What kind of business is this?

36. Some old cars, which no longer run, are stored in his yard.

37. I know the woman whom you ought to see.

38. Vote for the referendum which is most likely to solve the problem.

39. One of my brothers lives in Philadelphia.

40. My uncle bought the refrigerator that was most moderately priced.

41. The clock, which I had fixed, has stopped again.

42. Two little boys whom we knew came to see us.

43. Our friends, about whom we were speaking, left for South Dakota.

44. Her greatest skill is in the one-hundred-meter race.

45. Tell the police officer, who will stop the traffic.

46. The mountain peak, which we climbed, was entirely bare.

47. We must learn to respect her wishes.

48. One should not be controlled by fear.

49. Let us invite all the children who live nearby.

50. On the coast, days that begin with fog may often change to sun.

51. Don't touch the dog that is growling.

52. The letters that he forgot are now too old to send.

53. The hardware clerk has plenty of others.

54. The pool, near which we were playing, was very shallow.

55. He asked for any job that was available.

56. The pond, which I circled on foot, is covered with algae.

57. Our doorbell has something the matter with it.

58. Let us be grateful for favors that we receive.

59. Whose is this torn geography book?

60. Neither of the teams was able to make a score.

61. These letters, which have just come, are not ours.

62. The girls who are playing basketball enjoy the game.

63. The tunnel, through which the train sped, was very long and dark.

64. A gardener, whom we knew, gave us a dozen bulbs.

65. Which of these books should I buy for Monica?

66. The university honors this student, in whose memory the scholarship fund is started.

67. Catch the rascal who has spray-painted the wall.

68. They had warned you many times of the deep water.

69. The road by which we hoped to go was closed for repairs.

70. The game, which he invented, resembled checkers.

71. Whom did you meet at the football game?

72. He and I spent a very pleasant day in Friendship, Maine.

73. They knew who had sent them the gift.

74. The snow that fell caused the garage roof to cave in.

75. The tickets for which we applied are free.

76. The comedian, at whose jokes we laughed, was short and lively.

77. An old man, to whom the child ran, stood at the door.

78. Did you notice who came into the room?

79. Each child whom I call may go to the gym.

80. The patient about whom she inquired was much improved.

81. Not a single player knew what the coach meant.

82. We did not dare to ask your grandmother for a piece of pie.

83. The path on which we rode our bikes was very straight and smooth.

84. The darkness, which is falling, will end the search.

85. I have not seen toys like these for many years.

86. Athletes who are paid large sums of money do not always perform well.

87. The books that we most enjoy are mystery stories.

88. The little boy spoke to everyone whom he passed.

89. Either of your parents must sign this report card.

90. Father was happy to meet the friends whom I brought.

91. Is it true that people who know the most often say the least?

92. Whose are these?

93. Mary, whose mother is ill, helps dress her brothers and sister.

94. My father scarcely expected to meet us there.

95. The employer for whom we work gives clear instructions.

96. Those are very delicious dishes.

97. Here is one watercolor that I painted last winter.

98. Did you identify the boy whom I called?

99. Who calls in such a rude and angry voice?

100. What seems to be the matter with the cat?

101. The door, by which we entered, led into a large, sunny room.

102. Give this telescope to him.

103. None of the prizes could be awarded this year.

104. Will the rain that is coming spoil our bird-watching?

105. The snare-drum set about which they inquired has been sold.

106. I see who is hiding behind the kitchen door.

DEMONSTRATIVE ADJECTIVE

> A demonstrative adjective limits a noun by pointing out _which one._ There are four demonstrative adjectives: _this, that, these, those._

The demonstrative adjectives are underlined:

1. _This_ old car is always stalling.
2. _That_ black oak tree is a hundred years old.
3. _These_ rayon, checked shirts are made in India.
4. _Those_ portable radios seem very expensive.

Find the demonstrative adjectives:

1. Bill owns those two striped shirts.
2. This welcome rain has increased water in the reservoir.
3. These desperate and hungry people need help.
4. Please cut that broccoli into small pieces.
5. A sharp knife caused these deep gashes.
6. Let those boys leave for lunch.
7. I have just discovered this solution to the problem.
8. These trains carry many commuters every day.
9. Peggy made all that money as a lifeguard.
10. These new hairstyles are pretty wild.

POSSESSIVE ADJECTIVE

A possessive adjective shows ownership. These are the possessive adjectives: <u>my</u>, <u>our</u>, <u>your</u>, <u>his</u>, <u>her</u>, <u>its</u>, <u>their</u>.

The possessive adjectives are underlined:

1. <u>My</u> shoulder aches terribly.
2. <u>Her</u> mother just chatted with <u>your</u> mother.
3. He spoke eloquently of <u>their</u> proposal.
4. The tornado wreaked <u>its</u> fury on the town.
5. The gift of <u>his</u> library has benefited <u>our</u> school.

Find the possessive adjectives:

1. Her tone of voice was ingratiatingly pleasant.
2. We hope this card conveys our sympathy for you during your distressful illness.
3. The teacher was annoyed by the constant whispering.
4. Their estimate for painting our house seems fair.
5. I have just met my former French teacher.
6. The alligator opened its enormous jaws.
7. Have you read her list of questions yet?
8. Our amiable neighbors never object to the children.
9. The orchestra has begun its Friday concerts.
10. The nurse will examine your child now.

ADJECTIVE — COMPARATIVE DEGREE

> Adjectives use the comparative degree
> when one thing is compared with another.

Adjectives in the comparative degree are underlined:

1. Give the baby the smaller piece of bread.
2. Today is a grayer day than yesterday.
3. Of the two children, Steve is less noisy in the morning.
4. That wooden bridge becomes more unstable every year.
5. Here is a more recent copy of the magazine.

Find the adjectives in the comparative degree:

1. The fans are becoming more enthusiastic.

2. The north trail is more rugged than the south.

3. We have got to be calmer.

4. Then, a clearer idea occurred to him.

5. Is there a grander sight than Niagara Falls?

6. This spy novel is a more exciting book.

7. Throw the ball to the nearer base.

8. Have you ever heard of a more ridiculous excuse?

9. Copper is softer than iron.

10. The shorter man is older than the taller man.

11. The wiser choice would be to do the kindest thing.

12. This magazine is less appealing.

13. You become more difficult to reach by phone as time goes by.

14. Larry wears brighter clothes than his brother David.

15. I would advise you to use the better lawyer.

16. The thinner paint is more expensive.

17. The thicker paper lets through less light.

18. She is more outspoken than her husband.

19. The more original design will be used in this issue.

20. The month of January is usually colder than the month of November.

Use these adjectives in the comparative degree:

1. late	6. good	11. beneficial	16. indignant
2. shabby	7. stupid	12. quick	17. much
3. desolate	8. desirable	13. bad	18. indistinct
4. hasty	9. steep	14. prompt	19. peevish
5. angry	10. true	15. solitary	20. courteous

ADJECTIVE — SUPERLATIVE DEGREE

Adjectives use the superlative degree when
one thing is compared with two or more.

Adjectives in the superlative degree are underlined:

1. Eighty-five is our <u>highest</u> score.

2. That movie video is the <u>most amusing</u> I've seen this year.

3. The waltz is the <u>most graceful</u> dance.

4. The miser lived in the <u>meanest</u> shack.

5. This report is the <u>best</u> that I have heard.

Find the adjectives in the superlative degree:

1. Richard ranked highest in his class on the science test.

2. The conclusion to this book is the most exciting part.

3. Tuesday was the hottest day of August.

4. Why is it that only the wealthiest people can afford yachts?

5. This pair of glasses is the most accurate.

6. This year's Fourth of July celebration has been the most spectacular.

7. Jeanne is the best violinist in the school.

8. A good basketball player is not always the speediest.

9. This year the fall has been the wettest season.

Use these adjectives in the superlative degree:

1.	lively	18.	kind
2.	appropriate	19.	quiet
3.	valuable	20.	close
4.	jolly	21.	productive
5.	good	22.	dexterous
6.	crafty	23.	populous
7.	tight	24.	warm
8.	noble	25.	irregular
9.	bright	26.	bad
10.	alert	27.	fascinating
11.	near	28.	tidy
12.	sure	29.	tricky
13.	simple	30.	plain
14.	destructive	31.	uncivilized
15.	handsome	32.	delicate
16.	original	33.	radiant
17.	confident	34.	enduring

ADVERB MODIFYING A VERB

> An adverb modifies a verb.

The adverbs underlined modify verbs:

1. The citizens contributed <u>generously</u> to the fund.
2. The conductor led the orchestra <u>brilliantly</u>.
3. The elephant charged <u>furiously</u> at the hunter.
4. We <u>barely</u> recognized our old neighborhood.

Find the adverbs that modify verbs in these sentences:

1. The tea kettle steamed vigorously on the stove.
2. The late frost has completely killed those daffodils.
3. How skillfully the trumpeter improvised.
4. Mother scrubbed the vegetables vigorously.
5. The children are playing together harmoniously.
6. Dropping his tools to the floor, the old workman wearily sat down.
7. The crowd at the game cheered wildly.
8. Peevishly the tycoon acknowledged he had been cheating.
9. The corn ripened slowly under the hot August sun.
10. Leaving the sheltered bay, the boat cautiously approached open water.

Use these adverbs to modify verbs:

1.	admirably	18.	dubiously
2.	decorously	19.	fastidiously
3.	laboriously	20.	appropriately
4.	pungently	21.	impulsively
5.	sparsely	22.	impartially
6.	extravagantly	23.	abominably
7.	placidly	24.	characteristically
8.	caustically	25.	paternally
9.	indispensably	26.	temporarily
10.	fallaciously	27.	critically
11.	apprehensively	28.	mysteriously
12.	transiently	29.	symmetrically
13.	fantastically	30.	conclusively
14.	significantly	31.	enviously
15.	enthusiastically	32.	optimistically
16.	amply	33.	memorably
17.	obscurely	34.	adventurously

ADVERB MODIFYING AN ADJECTIVE
Adverb of Degree

An adverb modifies an adjective.

The adverbs underlined modify adjectives and are called adverbs of degree:

1. A <u>severely</u> injured worker lay on the stretcher.
2. The news story was <u>unmistakably</u> controversial.
3. They <u>openly</u> refused to obey the order.
4. International aid workers finished building a <u>fully</u> equipped hospital just in time.
5. The speaker's words were <u>immoderately</u> critical.

Find the adverbs modifying adjectives:

1. A neatly dressed child appeared at the door.
2. The doctor comforted the sorely stricken father.
3. Be careful of this newly varnished floor.
4. He was playing a strangely familiar song.
5. Shall we go to this widely advertised lecture?
6. What a deliciously flavored pie!
7. With prematurely gray hair he looked older than he was.
8. The rescue succeeded because of a boldly conceived plan.
9. So much unhappiness has come from the falsely reported news.

10. We thought the referee's decision was incredibly unfair.

11. A gratefully murmured response let her know her gift was on time.

Use these adverbs to modify adjectives:

1. rather	13. badly	25. indifferently
2. entirely	14. exceedingly	26. urgently
3. somewhat	15. highly	27. supremely
4. probably	16. unusually	28. truly
5. undoubtedly	17. moderately	29. hopelessly
6. quite	18. incompletely	30. essentially
7. dangerously	19. imperfectly	31. gravely
8. perfectly	20. unfairly	32. dishonorably
9. exceptionally	21. distinctly	33. emphatically
10. brilliantly	22. commonly	34. unquestionably
11. scarcely	23. partially	35. doubly
12. frequently	24. tolerably	36. progressively

ADVERB MODIFYING ANOTHER ADVERB
Adverb of Degree

An adverb modifies another adverb.

The adverbs underlined modify other adverbs; they are called adverbs of degree.

1. The blizzard struck the city <u>most</u> unexpectedly.
2. The teacher spoke <u>rather</u> sadly to the class.
3. The truck with medicines <u>headed</u> directly south.
4. The child's mother watched <u>more</u> anxiously.
5. The busy operator replied <u>almost</u> impatiently.

Find the adverbs that modify other adverbs:

1. The ideas in this paper are expressed quite clearly.
2. The boy ran much faster than the puppy.
3. Have you studied the lesson carefully enough?
4. The mayor spoke fairly eloquently.
5. The sun shines too brightly upon the page.
6. His excuse was less favorably received.
7. The pupils laughed so heartily at the joke.
8. The huge gray elephant moved very slowly.
9. Mother spoke somewhat crossly.
10. I shall listen most intently for the bell.

11. Renee sings passably well.

12. You are speaking rather fast.

13. She opened her eyes too quickly.

14. The boy answered somewhat impolitely.

15. By using a cane, the patient walked moderately well.

16. The radio announcer learned to speak extremely clearly.

17. Don't you feel you are driving excessively fast?

18. On this test I succeeded vastly better.

Use these adverbs to modify other adverbs:

1.	too	11.	much
2.	least	12.	hardly
3.	less	13.	rather
4.	almost	14.	fairly
5.	more	15.	scarcely
6.	most	16.	enough
7.	somewhat	17.	half
8.	very	18.	merely
9.	quite	19.	indifferently
10.	so	20.	unmistakably

ADVERB — COMPARATIVE DEGREE

> Adverbs use the comparative degree when
> one thing is compared with another.

Adverbs in the comparative degree are underlined:

1. An airplane travels <u>faster</u> than a train.
2. The sailboat came <u>closer</u> to the rock than I thought.
3. This week Roger promised to study <u>harder.</u>
4. You will have to knock <u>more vigorously</u> this time.
5. The wind is blowing <u>more gently</u> today.

Find the adverbs in the comparative degree:

1. Do you think Tom acts more suspiciously than he did?
2. Tomorrow Mary will report more thoroughly on the Industrial Revolution.
3. These girls are likely to work more carefully than those boys.
4. If you do not study, you will be marked worse tomorrow.
5. The teacher seemed to speak more sternly than usual.
6. The motor runs better since the mechanic tuned it.
7. We laughed more heartily than they did.
8. When we moved to a larger apartment, we were more comfortably settled than before.
9. At the roar of the crowd, the team fought more energetically.
10. This answer is more probably the correct one.

Use these adverbs in the comparative degree:

1.	frantically	18.	well
2.	early	19.	pleasantly
3.	often	20.	prudently
4.	tenaciously	21.	sluggishly
5.	moderately	22.	clamorously
6.	far	23.	carelessly
7.	badly	24.	indolently
8.	carefully	25.	wisely
9.	suspiciously	26.	likely
10.	miserably	27.	tediously
11.	recently	28.	buoyantly
12.	quietly	29.	tolerantly
13.	negligently	30.	generously
14.	resolutely	31.	heatedly
15.	abundantly	32.	gently
16.	vivaciously	33.	briskly
17.	radiantly	34.	narrowly

ADVERB — SUPERLATIVE DEGREE

> Adverbs use the superlative degree when a thing is compared with two or more other things, or when it shows emphasis.

Adverbs in the superlative degree are underlined:

1. Of all the class, Valerie studies most faithfully.
2. On the third day of the storm, the wind blew most tempestuously.
3. The researcher labored most tenaciously in her lab.
4. Alice played the piano most skillfully of all.
5. The truck hoisted the load most satisfactorily.

Find the adverbs in the superlative degree:

1. Of all the seasons, summer is the one enjoyed most enthusiastically.
2. Except for a few, all the pupils listened most attentively.
3. That company has pursued the contract most aggressively.
4. Flowers grow most luxuriantly in this sunny spot.
5. Sharon was dressed earliest.
6. The grocer has succeeded most prosperously.
7. The lion tore his food most ravenously.
8. Most gladly will I lend you what you need.
9. The carpenter repaired the fence most carelessly.
10. The rain beat most fiercely upon our windows.

Use these adverbs in the superlative degree:

1.	furiously	18.	humanely
2.	badly	19.	incredulously
3.	narrowly	20.	monotonously
4.	sagaciously	21.	gratefully
5.	extravagantly	22.	fragrantly
6.	cruelly	23.	successfully
7.	cowardly	24.	prudently
8.	affectionately	25.	honorably
9.	emotionally	26.	maliciously
10.	vitally	27.	well
11.	delicately	28.	negligently
12.	thoughtlessly	29.	exceptionally
13.	conspicuously	30.	obscurely
14.	felicitously	31.	unfavorably
15.	ravenously	32.	dismally
16.	proudly	33.	joyously
17.	improvidently	34.	urgently

ADVERB REVIEW

Here are various adverbs for use in sentences:

1.	upward	17.	flawlessly
2.	incompletely	18.	early
3.	unquestionably	19.	penitently
4.	jointly	20.	less
5.	tolerantly	21.	ignobly
6.	much	22.	conclusively
7.	neutrally	23.	somewhat
8.	forward	24.	anywhere
9.	oddly	25.	faultlessly
10.	unusually	26.	soon
11.	supremely	27.	utterly
12.	acutely	28.	actively
13.	frequently	29.	quite
14.	successively	30.	mechanically
15.	too	31.	permanently
16.	periodically	32.	legitimately

33.	very	51.	scarcely
34.	eternally	52.	appropriately
35.	dramatically	53.	inadequately
36.	strenuously	54.	south
37.	strongly	55.	sometimes
38.	shrewdly	56.	tenaciously
39.	again	57.	offensively
40.	vocally	58.	fiercely
41.	enough	59.	pathetically
42.	artistically	60.	least
43.	contemptibly	61.	silently
44.	rather	62.	home
45.	immortally	63.	there
46.	obviously	64.	unfairly
47.	tomorrow	65.	away
48.	reasonably	66.	incessantly
49.	apparently	67.	always
50.	harmoniously	68.	joyously

COORDINATE CONJUNCTION

> Coordinate conjunctions join words or
> groups of words of equal rank.

The coordinate conjunctions are underlined:

1. he <u>and</u> I
2. not John <u>but</u> Richard
3. Boston <u>or</u> San Francisco
4. We did not study <u>nor</u> did the teacher demand it.
5. He is sick, <u>yet</u> he is alert.

Find the coordinate conjunctions:

1. The spring frost was severe, but not all the flowers have died.
2. Is she coming early or late?
3. Wednesday was rainy and cold.
4. Bring me a hammer or an axe.
5. The fire was quenched, but the damage was extensive.
6. The sun is hot, yet the breeze keeps us comfortable.
7. Rubbers or boots are needed today.
8. The patient needed help, but he saw no one near.
9. The fullback can pass or run or kick.
10. Tonight we must study Latin and history and spelling.

11. I understand, but I am not convinced.

12. We hurried to the depot, yet we missed the train.

13. Peaches, pears, and plums are now in the supermarkets.

14. The bakery sold bread, rolls, and pies.

15. The engineer didn't see the signal and failed to apply the brakes.

16. The tire is damaged but not beyond repair.

17. The driver cried out, and the pedestrian stared in horror.

18. They have not cooked nor cleaned for a week.

19. He was adjudged guilty, but it was a poor decision.

20. You may choose vanilla or chocolate or strawberry.

21. The rain does not stop, nor does the wind diminish.

22. The children ate a large meal, yet they still wanted dessert.

23. That play has been performed at home and abroad.

24. You must not loiter or you will be late!

25. Has Fred come, or Joseph, or Tom?

26. I need a good pen and half a dozen pencils.

27. The car looked old, but the engine was good.

28. Quick! Call Susan or Joe!

CORRELATIVE CONJUNCTION

> Correlative conjunctions are coordinate conjunctions that are used in pairs.

The correlative conjunctions are underlined:

1. The child is <u>both</u> inquisitive <u>and</u> energetic.
2. <u>Neither</u> snow <u>nor</u> frost can deter the travelers.
3. <u>Either</u> the alarm clock <u>or</u> my brother will awaken us.
4. You may have <u>not only</u> the chest, <u>but also</u> whatever is in it.

Find the correlative conjunctions:

1. The lawyer will either write or telephone.
2. Neither algebra nor geometry is too difficult.
3. Elizabeth not only sings well but she acts, too.
4. Both milk and cheese are harmful to people with artery disease.
5. I have neither their phone number nor their address.
6. Tim has lost both his cap and his mittens.
7. Not only rain but also hail beat upon our garden.
8. You will need a doctor's appointment not only tomorrow but also next week.
9. The policeman neither saw the man nor spoke to him.
10. Either Mel or Tom is working in the warehouse.

11. Buy either a pie or a cake.

12. Both the television and the radio need repairs.

13. Either work on your lesson now, or stay after school!

14. Sara and Tom not only earn good money, but they also save it.

15. Neither crying babies nor barking dogs are easy to listen to for long.

16. At the museum we enjoyed both the paintings and the photographs.

17. Mom wants from you not only a phone call but also some letters.

18. Gary neither swims nor dives.

19. Could I have both vanilla and chocolate?

20. My coat is either in the sunroom or in the hall.

21. Tell the newsboy to leave both the Globe and the Herald.

22. Not only boys but also girls enjoy skating.

23. You may choose either a picnic or the movies.

24. Neither the doctor nor the nurse can come.

25. The winter brings both deep snow and thick ice.

26. George works either in Boston or in Quincy.

27. I see not only the moon but also three planets.

28. Neither Tuesday nor Wednesday is a good day for me to meet you.

SUBORDINATE CONJUNCTION

> A subordinate conjunction connects a
> subordinate clause with a principal clause.

The subordinate conjunctions are underlined:

1. It will rain, <u>if</u> the weather predictions are accurate.

2. <u>Unless</u> they save some money, they will be hard pressed.

3. We watched from the street <u>while</u> the house burned.

4. <u>Before</u> the war ends, many soldiers will die.

5. <u>Although</u> the bell has rung, we shall not be marked tardy.

Find the subordinate conjunctions:

1. When the alarm clock rang, the boy uttered a groan and turned over.

2. Our travel agent could not say whether we would reach Ohio by four in the afternoon.

3. Since the week has been so stormy, we appreciate today's sunlight.

4. Uncle Paul wore a wool muffler lest he catch cold.

5. The naturalist can tell where black bears hibernate.

6. If I had five dollars, I would buy some skates.

7. The mechanic showed me where he had patched the tire.

8. Before you forget it, return my book.

9. Although the lake is rough, I am going for a sail.

10. None of us knew why Rhonda became fatigued so quickly.

11. I cannot help you unless you tell me the truth.

12. Though the days are getting shorter, it is still quite warm.

13. While the sun is bright, let me show you our garden.

14. When he spoke, I knew something was wrong.

15. After the party was over, Mary had quite a headache.

16. While he was speaking, my mind was on something else.

17. The nurse walked quietly lest she disturb the patient.

18. While the boy was reading, he felt he was in another world.

19. The counselor warned Jim because he liked the boy.

20. After we reach our cottage, your vacation will begin.

21. Since darkness was falling, we could not fix the gate.

22. The unemployed truck driver offered to work wherever he could.

23. Although Natalie worked hard, the garden didn't thrive this year.

24. If you meet my brother, remind him of that errand.

25. Unless we clean up the rooms together, this place will be a mess.

26. Since the thermometer was dropping, Father built a fire.

27. Until Tom's letter came today, we had not heard from him for weeks.

VERB — PERSON AND NUMBER

> Verbs have first, second, and third persons;
> singular and plural number.

	Singular	Plural
First person:	I call	we call
Second person:	you call	you call
Third person:	he, she, it calls	they call

Find the person and number of the following verbs:

1. she had designed
2. we have detected
3. he was diving
4. I have concealed
5. they were learning
6. he had fastened
7. I shall be called
8. she stumbles
9. we have been summoned
10. she shall choose
11. they are paid
12. they had been admonished
13. we were chopping
14. he shall be awarded
15. I have been shown
16. you were being hit
17. he was practicing
18. we shall be praised
19. they had written
20. it ticks
21. you are being watched
22. I shall succeed
23. they march
24. we had been warned

25.	they cook	41.	it had been repaired
26.	I swim	42.	I shall have counted
27.	they shall be judged	43.	she had been invited
28.	you have noticed	44.	you had demonstrated
29.	we shall try	45.	she shall have been called
30.	he has been questioned	46.	we scamper
31.	I had decided	47.	they shall have been dismissed
32.	you speak	48.	he has imagined
33.	they have been teased	49.	we study
34.	she was being admired	50.	you are frightened
35.	you shall observe	51.	they are hired
36.	it is broken	52.	she has been taught
37.	you have been deceived	53.	I was being scolded
38.	we were being chased	54.	it had been dropped
39.	they have observed	55.	we shall have studied
40.	you struggle	56.	they were being marked

VERB — PRESENT TENSE

A verb in the present tense
shows action in present time.

Verbs in the present tense are underlined:

1. The tennis finalists <u>contend</u> for the prize.

2. A silver moon <u>is rising</u> above the trees.

3. Sharon and Jack <u>buy</u> groceries at the corner market.

4. My grandfather usually <u>plays</u> golf on the weekend.

5. Martha's poodle <u>is being clipped.</u>

Find the verbs in the present tense:

1. The singer breathes deeply before going on stage.

2. The lenses are being ground for a telescope.

3. Jackson struggles with the problem.

4. The quarterback is removed from the game.

5. Our cat is snoozing in her favorite chair.

6. This bonus augments your salary.

7. See how that fisherman hurls his line to a specific spot?

8. Dick is working on math problems.

9. The bullfrog inflates his cheeks.

Use these verbs in the present tense, either active or passive voice.

1. protest	18. encircle	35. increase
2. investigate	19. annoy	36. extricate
3. forgive	20. examine	37. smooth
4. decay	21. lighten	38. dissolve
5. stumble	22. cook	39. disguise
6. pretend	23. speculate	40. cultivate
7. construct	24. design	41. yawn
8. skulk	25. hesitate	42. call
9. discourage	26. hold	43. mutter
0. respond	27. sustain	44. alarm
1. yield	28. freeze	45. quiver
2. diminish	29. blunder	46. eliminate
3. sketch	30. subside	47. embellish
4. compute	31. arrange	48. discover
5. illuminate	32. accomplish	49. animate
6. prepare	33. establish	50. gleam
7. escape	34. defraud	51. relish

VERB — PAST TENSE

> A verb in the past tense
> shows action in past time.

Verbs in the past tense are underlined:

1. Thunder <u>rumbled</u> above, and we all <u>ran</u> for shelter.
2. Fresh lobsters <u>were being packed</u> in barrels.
3. Last summer we <u>sailed</u> on Penobscot Bay.
4. The candle <u>was fluttering</u> in the wind.
5. The hikers <u>were soaked</u> in the heavy downpour.

Find the verbs in the past tense:

1. All the workers in that department were wearing safety helmets.
2. They sat all day working from video display terminals.
3. The bus pulled away just now.
4. Where were you hiding?
5. Exhaust from all the morning traffic clogged the air.
6. Reluctantly, she called the dentist for an appointment.
7. I was visiting my friend in the hospital.
8. Snow was falling heavily all night.
9. The trash dumpster was being emptied right beneath our window.
10. Two men were repairing a hole in the street.

Use these verbs in the past tense, either active or passive voice.

1. drink	18. prohibit	35. duplicate
2. satisfy	19. forecast	36. deceive
3. imitate	20. forgive	37. suppose
4. anticipate	21. adjust	38. invent
5. predict	22. teach	39. mutilate
6. create	23. scar	40. abandon
7. deface	24. strengthen	41. emancipate
8. establish	25. extricate	42. irritate
9. discharge	26. scour	43. erase
10. haunt	27. terrify	44. defy
11. grope	28. contribute	45. relent
12. attain	29. provoke	46. adorn
13. wheeze	30. stumble	47. compute
14. amble	31. accumulate	48. secure
15. persuade	32. encircle	49. grasp
16. donate	33. hire	50. admit
17. award	34. announce	51. relax

VERB — FUTURE TENSE

A verb in the future tense
shows action in future time.

Verbs in the future tense are underlined:

1. The condominium <u>will be sold</u> next Saturday.

2. I <u>shall not see</u> such courage again.

3. We <u>will pause</u> now for a short break.

4. The refugees <u>will be</u> sheltered here.

5. This line <u>will bisect</u> the angle.

Find the verbs in the future tense:

1. If we walk in the woods, we shall be tormented by mosquitoes.

2. The message will be transmitted to your family.

3. Tonight our dinner will be cooked in the microwave.

4. I shall expect you at six o'clock.

5. You shall sit alone until recess.

6. Tonight the pond will freeze.

7. I will not allow you to go alone.

8. We shall reconcile our differences.

9. The news will be broadcast at noon.

Note: In modern usage, <u>shall</u> and <u>will</u> seldom retain the distinction between simple futurity and determination. If the distinction is required, consult any detailed grammar.

Use these verbs in the future tense, either active or passive voice.

1.	cheer	18.	employ	35.	win
2.	reject	19.	study	36.	practice
3.	tap	20.	rejoice	37.	catch
4.	scowl	21.	repair	38.	saunter
5.	snatch	22.	scold	39.	fly
6.	challenge	23.	borrow	40.	dig
7.	furnish	24.	whisper	41.	visit
8.	transfer	25.	repeat	42.	invent
9.	avert	26.	admire	43.	discourage
10.	resound	27.	acknowledge	44.	wither
11.	welcome	28.	hammer	45.	save
12.	search	29.	steal	46.	repay
13.	deplore	30.	weave	47.	salute
14.	whine	31.	crouch	48.	snarl
15.	entangle	32.	bombard	49.	pledge
16.	identify	33.	classify	50.	instruct
17.	growl	34.	offend	51.	haggle

VERB — PRESENT PERFECT

A verb in the present perfect tense
shows completed action in past time.

Verbs in the present perfect tense are underlined:

1. The hurricane <u>has passed</u> out to sea.
2. Many people <u>have invested</u> their money in stocks and bonds.
3. I <u>have</u> just <u>finished</u> all these difficult examples.
4. The taillights of their car <u>have disappeared</u> into the darkness.
5. The last meal of the day <u>has been served</u>.

Find the verbs in the present perfect tense:

1. The shoes have not been repaired by the cobbler.
2. The meeting of the city council has not started yet.
3. The gates to the park have been closed an hour.
4. Not a sound has been heard from the room.
5. The grocer has saved some fish for you.
6. The fog has settled in the river valley.
7. The morning paper has not been delivered.
8. A red signal has appeared in the sky.

Use these verbs in the present perfect tense, active or passive:

1. excite	18. praise	35. expand
2. quote	19. teach	36. sharpen
3. test	20. lie	37. warm
4. honor	21. exaggerate	38. foam
5. excel	22. develop	39. revive
6. grow	23. defend	40. free
7. construct	24. remit	41. complete
8. answer	25. operate	42. vindicate
9. gladden	26. exempt	43. deplore
0. envy	27. amaze	44. fight
1. disturb	28. ring	45. abuse
2. quarrel	29. hurt	46. denounce
3. love	30. detonate	47. reveal
4. rehearse	31. encircle	48. polish
5. shroud	32. bury	49. smother
6. leak	33. watch	50. whisper
7. vanish	34. hire	51. strive

VERB — PAST PERFECT

A verb in the past perfect tense shows completed action that had taken place at some past time.

Verbs in the past perfect tense are underlined:

1. The doctor <u>had been called</u> three times.
2. I <u>had</u> not <u>seen</u> that friend for two years.
3. The storm <u>had subsided</u> at midnight.
4. The morning newspaper <u>had come</u>.
5. The painters <u>had finished</u> the job.

Find the verbs in the past perfect tense:

1. The friends had expected to meet her at the station.
2. The fire had been set by two naughty children.
3. Every tree in the yard had been damaged by the frost.
4. At the time, our cottage had not been rented.
5. The high school pupils had been permitted to attend the show.
6. Not for many years had we enjoyed such a picnic.
7. The motorist had not discerned the train in the fog.
8. The reinforced bridge structure had withstood the seismic tremors of the earthquake.

Use these verbs in the past perfect tense, active or passive:

1. hate	18. guess	35. confide
2. surround	19. placate	36. encourage
3. chatter	20. shudder	37. secure
4. hoard	21. continue	38. fulfill
5. wander	22. protest	39. border
6. cheat	23. foresee	40. depart
7. sharpen	24. save	41. discard
8. erase	25. devour	42. evict
9. shout	26. execute	43. charge
10. succeed	27. banish	44. animate
11. stop	28. exhaust	45. elevate
12. choke	29. choose	46. neglect
13. earn	30. eradicate	47. dodge
14. stutter	31. expire	48. release
15. disappear	32. mount	49. proceed
16. annoy	33. ignore	50. decorate
17. exhale	34. baffle	51. stimulate

VERB — FUTURE PERFECT

A verb in the future perfect tense shows action that will have been completed before a time in the future.

Verbs in the future perfect tense are underlined:

1. By tomorrow I <u>shall have answered</u> the letter.

2. Before darkness falls, the pupils <u>shall have been dismissed</u>.

3. Before Monday evening, we <u>shall have learned</u> the truth.

4. When the bell has rung, he <u>shall have</u> already <u>gone</u>.

5. They <u>shall have traveled</u> a hundred miles by next week.

Find the verbs in the future perfect tense:

1. By December the class shall have finished the book.

2. Our car registration shall have been renewed by next summer.

3. By this evening he will have finished the job.

4. At the end of a few minutes your tooth will have been pulled.

5. In a moment we shall have finished the job.

6. With one more effort you will have won the prize.

7. When the rain stops, the books will have been ruined.

8. By tonight, I shall have bought two tickets.

Use these verbs in the future perfect tense, active or passive:

1.	avoid	18.	devote	35.	conclude
2.	hamper	19.	cheer	36.	furnish
3.	engage	20.	promote	37.	cook
4.	anger	21.	trespass	38.	question
5.	steal	22.	finish	39.	name
6.	mark	23.	settle	40.	divert
7.	issue	24.	salute	41.	share
8.	apply	25.	strive	42.	cease
9.	occupy	26.	kindle	43.	inflame
10.	invest	27.	bind	44.	balance
11.	decree	28.	bite	45.	shuffle
12.	deflate	29.	provide	46.	stumble
13.	delight	30.	mistake	47.	explode
14.	cancel	31.	flee	48.	measure
15.	decide	32.	find	49.	meet
16.	come	33.	tell	50.	do
17.	see	34.	hurt	51.	call

VERB — MOOD

> A verb has three moods -
> indicative, imperative, and subjunctive.

These verbs are in the indicative mood because they make a statement or ask a question:

1. Mount Fuji <u>arose</u> majestically from the plain.

2. <u>Isn't</u> his conduct rather questionable?

These verbs are in the imperative mood because they give a command:

3. <u>Do</u> nothing hasty or violent.

4. <u>Fasten</u> the garage door securely.

These verbs are in the subjunctive mood because they express a wish or a condition contrary to fact:

5. Joanne wishes that she <u>be chosen</u> chairperson.

6. If he <u>were</u> rich, would he buy a house?

Find the verbs in the following sentences and identify the mood of each:

1. Watch this luggage for half an hour.

2. A shadowy mouse scampered through the grass.

3. If the rivers overflow, the villages are doomed.

4. The pilot wished that he were certain of the weather.

5. Separate the large potatoes from the small.

6. The young girl confided in her teacher.

7. The motorists gazed in awe at the deep valley.

8. If the street were known, we could locate the house.

9. Broadcast the news of the victory this evening.

10. The neighbors organized a street fair.

11. Finish all your homework.

12. I wish I were taller!

13. The bully boasted of his cowardly tricks.

14. Spread the paint a little faster.

15. If my mother were home, she would pay you.

16. Sam wished that he had been taught correctly.

17. The complicated street plan challenged our sense of direction.

18. Don't talk while you chew your food!

19. If you acquiesce in the plan, I will help you.

20. The trip to Florida provided us with many enjoyable experiences.

21. If I were you, I would try another route.

22. The teacher readily approved the suggestion of the class.

23. If you converse, do it quietly.

VERB REVIEW

Try to identify the tense and mood of the verbs in the following sentences:

1. Aunt Sarah will expect us for dinner on Sunday.

2. The wharf was damaged by the tremendous waves.

3. Every streetlight had been extinguished by the power failure.

4. I shall visit my uncle during the spring vacation.

5. The captain kicked the football high into the air.

6. Traffic tonight is very heavy on the highway.

7. For a long time the lawyer sat at her desk.

8. Will the tailor have pressed my clothes by this afternoon?

9. After an exhausting day, the nurse sank gratefully into the chair.

10. The Chicago train will depart at noon from Track Five.

11. Show this applicant the way to the personnel office.

12. The howling dog was locked in the yard.

13. Without doubt Reagan was a popular president, he told her.

14. Elizabeth was frosting the cake for his birthday.

15. This machine separates cream from the milk.

16. She was sewing her new dress all afternoon.

96

17. A flock of ducks had just flown across the sky.

18. By tomorrow you will have received their decision.

19. We have often telephoned to friends in New York.

20. The Children's Museum awarded our dance troupe highest honors.

21. The sun seemed hotter and hotter.

22. The computer programmer revised the information easily.

23. A rotten elm was being sawed down by the work crew.

24. My grandparents will arrive tomorrow for Thanksgiving.

25. The yield of potatoes has increased on this organic farm.

26. These heavy winds generally subside about sundown.

27. He had been called too often for his own good.

28. An old man and his dog ambled along the walking path around the lake.

29. Eight small ducks are splashing on the edge of the lake.

30. At least by then, we shall have learned the truth.

31. Anne was practicing her first piano piece.

32. The little boy promised his mother a birthday gift.

33. The radio operator handed the mesage to the captain.

34. Joan has become very clever as a pianist.

35. The carpenter had repaired the front steps.

36. Three new books will be sent to you free.

37. A mysterious light is seen deep in the woods.

38. A downpour of rain drummed upon the tent.

39. A very good friend has given Richard a new radio.

40. They shall have delivered the groceries by five o'clock.

41. Will you please hand me the thread and needle?

42. This butter tastes very odd to me.

43. The telegram has already been delivered.

44. The athlete runs with ease and confidence.

45. Two mischievous boys were scribbling on the wall.

46. Last night's frost has blackened the flowers.

47. The workmen have completed our new garage.

48. We must repair the seat of this leather chair.

49. You have been awarded second prize.

50. For a long time the chess players watched the board.

51. A fine banjo clock is ticking on the wall.

52. The room was being flooded by the rising moonlight.

53. At the library he was looking for a copy of his favorite magazine.

54. Some leather-bound books will be sent to you.

55. He waited impatiently for the morning mail.

56. The traffic is stopped by that accident up ahead.

57. The crowd of fans was running across the field.

58. They will be entertained at the football stadium.

59. We were watching the front gate all afternoon.

60. That naughty boy has broken this valuable lamp.

61. She will not be convinced by all your excuses.

62. The Charles River drained into Boston Harbor.

63. The flowers bloomed very early this spring.

64. Have I not been punished enough?

65. A carved wooden statue from Africa stands upon my desk.

66. My father drinks coffee every morning.

67. A small black shadow prowled through the tall weeds by the house.

68. If I were energetic, I would gladly go with you.

VERB FORMS

Regular verbs form their principal parts by adding -d or -ed to the present tense.

These are the principal parts of a regular verb:

present: <u>call</u>   past: <u>called</u>   past participle: <u>called</u>

Irregular verbs form their principal parts in irregular ways. These are the principal parts of the commonly used irregular verbs:

PRESENT	PAST	PAST PARTICIPLE
am	was	been
awake	awoke (awaked)	awakened
begin	began	begun
bet	bet	bet
bind	bound	bound
bit	bit	bitten
blow	blew	blown
break	broke	broken
bring	brought	brought
burst	burst	burst
catch	caught	caught

PRESENT	PAST	PAST PARTICIPLE
choose	chose	chosen
come	came	come
creep	crept	crept
do	did	done
draw	drew	drawn
drink	drank	drunk
drive	drove	driven
eat	ate	eaten
fall	fell	fallen
flee	fled	fled
fly	flew	flown
forget	forgot	forgotten
freeze	froze	frozen
give	gave	given
go	went	gone
grow	grew	grown
hang	hung	hung

VERB FORMS

PRESENT	PAST	PAST PARTICIPLE
hurt	hurt	hurt
kneel	knelt (kneeled)	knelt (kneeled)
knit	knit (knitted)	knit (knitted)
know	knew	known
lay	laid	laid
lead	led	led
lie (recline)	lay	lain
light	lighted (lit)	lighted (lit)
ride	rode	ridden
ring	rang	rung
rise	rose	risen
run	ran	run
see	saw	seen
seek	sought	sought
shake	shook	shaken
show	showed	shown (showed)

PRESENT	PAST	PAST PARTICIPLE
sing	sang	sung
sink	sank	sunk
sit	sat	sat
sleep	slept	slept
slide	slid	slid
smell	smelled (smelt)	smelled (smelt)
sow	sowed	sown (sowed)
speak	spoke	spoken
steal	stole	stolen
stick	stuck	stuck
stride	strode	stridden
swim	swam	swum
teach	taught	taught
tear	tore	torn
throw	threw	thrown
wear	wore	worn
weave	wove	woven

CONJUGATION OF VERB

Conjugation of the verb <u>know</u>

Principal parts:
- present: know
- past: knew
- past participle: known

INDICATIVE MOOD

ACTIVE VOICE	PASSIVE VOICE
Present Tense	**Present Tense**
I know	I am known
you know	you are known
he, she, it knows	he, she, it is known
we know	we are known
you know	you are known
they know	they are known
Past Tense	**Past Tense**
I knew	I was known
you knew	you were known
he, she, it knew	he, she, it was known
we knew	we were known
you knew	you were known
they knew	they were known

ACTIVE VOICE	PASSIVE VOICE
Future Tense	Future Tense

I shall know	I shall be known
you will know	you will be known
he, she, it will know	he, she, it will be known
we shall know	we shall be known
you will know	you will be known
they will know	they will be known

Present Perfect Tense	Present Perfect Tense

I have known	I have been known
you have known	you have been known
he, she, it has known	he, she, it has been known
we have known	we have been known
you have known	you have been known
they have known	they have been known

Past Perfect Tense	Past Perfect Tense

I had known	I had been known
you had known	you had been known
he, she, it had known	he, she, it had been known
we had known	we had been known
you had known	you had been known
they had known	they had been known

Future Perfect Tense	Future Perfect Tense

I shall have known	I shall have been known
you will have known	you will have been known
he, she, it will have known	he, she, it will have been known
we shall have known	we shall have been known
you will have known	you will have been known
they will have known	they will have been known

SUBJUNCTIVE MOOD

ACTIVE VOICE

Present Tense

if I know
if you know
if he, she, it know

if we know
if you know
if they know

Past Tense

if I knew
if you knew
if he, she, it knew

if we knew
if you knew
if they knew

Present Perfect Tense

if I have known
if you have known
if he, she, it has known

if we have known
if you have known
if they have known

PASSIVE VOICE

Present Tense

if I be known
if you be known
if he, she, it be known

if we be known
if you be known
if they be known

Past Tense

if I were known
if you were known
if he, she, it were known

if we were known
if you were known
if they were known

Present Perfect Tense

if I have been known
if you have been known
if he, she, it has been known

if we have been known
if you have been known
if they have been known

ACTIVE VOICE	PASSIVE VOICE

Past Perfect Tense / Past Perfect Tense

Past Perfect Tense	Past Perfect Tense
if I had known	if I had been known
if you had known	if you had been known
if he, she, it had known	if he, she, it had been known
if we had known	if we had been known
if you had known	if you had been known
if they had known	if they had been known

IMPERATIVE MOOD

Present Tense	Present Tense
know	be known

INFINITIVES

Present Tense	Present Tense
to know	to be known

Perfect Tense	Perfect Tense
to have known	to have been known

PARTICIPLES

Present Tense	Present Tense
knowing	being known

Past Tense	Past Tense
known	known

Perfect Tense	Perfect Tense
having known	having been known

PARTICIPLE

> A participle is a verb form
> used as an adjective.

The participles are underlined:

1. <u>Seizing</u> the ball, the fullback ran thirty yards.

2. The detective, <u>having solved</u> the mystery, arrested the butler.

3. The catcher's thumb, <u>struck</u> by the ball, began to swell.

4. <u>Having been warned</u> of a steep drop, the motorist drove slowly.

5. Two <u>snarling</u> dogs are fighting in the schoolyard.

Find the participles in each sentence:

1. Frowning at the child, the salesclerk told her to keep her hands off the glass case.

2. Reminded of his boots, Peter reluctantly put them on.

3. Excused by the teacher, Amy dashed out of the room.

4. Having considered the offer, the man agreed to sell.

5. Peeking into the closet, Kathleen saw a new sled.

6. Having been gashed by a knife, I hurried to the emergency room.

7. The sun, rising at six o'clock, awakened me.

8. The bread, burnt to a crisp, could not be eaten.

9. The courier, biking adeptly through the heavy traffic, reached his destination on time.

10. His arm, lacerated by the sharp metal, bled near the elbow.

11. Disappointed with his marks, the boy scowled at his report card.

12. Having been encouraged, Mary sang another song.

13. Hiking on the mountain, the naturalist discovered some endangered flower species.

14. Having selected a suit, the customer tried on the coat.

15. The stars, twinkling in the sky, were bright and clear.

16. Separated from their guide, the German tourists felt lost.

17. Outwitted by the police, the robber surrendered.

18. The President's wife, conducted to the platform, prepared to speak.

19. Having dictated a letter, the manager picked up the telephone.

20. The tree, having been weakened by the hurricane, toppled to the ground in the next storm.

21. The boy, having some money from the babysitter, next begged to go to the store.

22. The visitor, hestitating at the threshold finally entered.

PARTICIPLE — PRESENT TENSE
Active and Passive Voice

A participle may be used in the present tense, in either the active or the passive voice.

The present active participles are underlined:

1. The mechanic, tapping the generator, found the loose wire.
2. Shouting with excitement, the boys plunged from the raft.

The present passive participles are underlined:

1. Being followed by a stranger, I hurried home.
2. Tom, being elected captain, stammered his thanks.

Find the present participle in each sentence. Is it active or passive?

1. Demanding his rent, the landlord became abusive.

2. Being frightened by the lightning, the child shrieked aloud.

3. The actor, being roundly applauded, took a curtain bow.

4. His finger, being infected, needs medical attention.

5. Pinching the flame, the camper extinguished the candle.

6. The swimmer, being ensnared by a net, cried out for help.

7. Being punctured by a tack, the tire went flat.

8. Whimpering with cold, the puppy scratched at the door.

9. Traversing the glacier, the climbers attacked the cliff.

10. Being weakened by the rain, the bridge collapsed into the river.

se these verbs in sentences as present participles, either active
r passive.

1.	oblige	10.	saunter	19.	baffle	28.	destroy
2.	entertain	11.	descend	20.	explore	29.	hint
3.	hook	12.	dart	21.	reinforce	30.	dissent
4.	weave	13.	outwit	22.	testify	31.	crawl
5.	wrestle	14.	repair	23.	utter	32.	complain
6.	bruise	15.	strengthen	24.	crash	33.	announce
7.	moan	16.	jog	25.	spoil	34.	add
8.	telephone	17.	blink	26.	probe	35.	sail
9.	coax	18.	trace	27.	tamper	36.	quit

PARTICIPLE — PAST TENSE
Passive Voice

A participle may be used in the past tense,
but only in the passive voice.

The past participles are underlined:

1. A fox, <u>caught</u> in the trap, was killed by the dogs.

2. The accident, although <u>described</u> by the driver, seemed incredible.

3. <u>Hurt</u> by the unkind remark, the girl hid her face.

4. The roof, <u>scorched</u> by the blaze, must be replaced.

5. The apple tree, <u>bent</u> with age, sweetened the air with its blossoms.

Find the participles in the past tense:

1. Wounded by shrapnel, the marine sank to the ground.

2. The carpenter, handicapped with arthritis, could no longer work.

3. The chimney, weakened in the fire, toppled into the flames.

4. The train, although announced, will not arrive for twenty minutes.

5. Separated from his mother, the child wandered along the street.

6. Dragged from the water, the swimmer was speedily revived.

7. The jewel, examined in better light, proved to be a diamond.

8. Observed in his mischief, the little boy ran away.

9. Erected at great expense, the stadium is to be dedicated in June.

10. His book, published in October, has already sold well.

n sentences, use the past participial forms of these verbs:

1.	capture	10.	mention	19.	scratch	28.	freeze
2.	remove	11.	float	20.	grow	29.	grow
3.	invent	12.	plow	21.	coerce	30.	choose
4.	prepare	13.	scale	22.	construct	31.	shake
5.	split	14.	follow	23.	file	32.	stick
6.	mark	15.	know	24.	embroider	33.	win
7.	worry	16.	see	25.	state	34.	write
8.	remind	17.	advise	26.	seek	35.	sing
9.	permit	18.	promise	27.	drive	36.	decorate

PARTICIPLE — PERFECT TENSE
Active and Passive Voice

A participle may be used in the perfect tense,
in either the active or the passive voice.

The perfect active participles are underlined:

1. The policeman, <u>having seen</u> the accident, called the ambulance.

2. <u>Having pocketed</u> the dollar, Tim headed for the store.

The perfect passive participles are underlined:

1. <u>Having been called</u>, the children hurried home.

2. The dog, <u>having been frightened</u> by the thunder, hid under the bed.

Find the perfect participle in each sentence. Is it active or passive?

1. Having been nourished by good food, the wanderer regained his strength.

2. Ned, having seen the money on the floor, picked it up.

3. The children, all having earned promotion, filed gaily to their new class.

4. First having been sanded, the floor was then varnished.

5. The French and Indians, having been defeated, surrendered to the English.

6. Having chattered half the night, the girls finally fell asleep.

7. Dick, having learned to caddy, now earns plenty of money.

8. Having been cracked by a heavy blow, the bell no longer rang.

9. Ted, having watered the garden, put the hose away.

10. The security guard, having seen a movement, peered into the darkness.

Use these verbs in sentences as perfect participles, either active or passive.

1.	call	10.	manage	19.	finish	28.	glimpse
2.	gaze	11.	copy	20.	compose	29.	excuse
3.	visit	12.	mend	21.	grasp	30.	rehearse
4.	judge	13.	deliver	22.	swindle	31.	pinch
5.	trace	14.	benefit	23.	confiscate	32.	correct
6.	advise	15.	seek	24.	proclaim	33.	infect
7.	shuffle	16.	bite	25.	discern	34.	create
8.	amble	17.	thread	26.	wiggle	35.	rescue
9.	flare	18.	mutter	27.	stumble	36.	rectify

PARTICIPLE WITH NOMINATIVE ABSOLUTE

> A participle with a noun or pronoun in the nominative case is often used in a nominative absolute phrase.

The participle and the nominative absolute are underlined:

1. The <u>money being lost</u>, the girls could not go to the movies.
2. The <u>class having been warned</u>, the children kept busy.
3. The <u>key having been found</u>, we entered the cottage.
4. The <u>tire being flat</u>, Ted had to walk two miles.
5. The <u>drought</u> at last <u>having been broken</u>, the fields grew green.

Find the participles and the nominative absolutes:

1. His attention wandering, the boy did not hear his name.

2. Her body being nourished by good food, the patient grew strong.

3. The soil having been turned over, I next turned to planting.

4. The hose being connected, the children enjoyed a sprinkling.

5. The pieces having been practiced, the concert went smoothly.

6. The dog having barked loudly, Mrs. Eaton rushed to the door.

7. The child being lost, the state troopers searched all day.

8. The bus having spewed black smoke, I stood choking in its aftermath.

9. The snow being too deep, we could not reach town.

10. The tire having been changed, we continued our trip to New York.

11. The police having confiscated the handguns, street shootings decreased a certain amount.

12. The cactus plants having blossomed, the desert was full of color.

13. The truck being heavily loaded, we made slow progress.

14. Two jets being high in the air, we saw long vapor trails.

15. The corn having been planted, I looked for rain.

16. The telephone ringing, the man leaped from his chair.

17. The sun being too hot for planting trees, the forester worked on other tasks.

18. The books having been placed on the desk, the teacher distributed the test.

19. Marble being too expensive, the library was made of granite.

20. The water being disconnected, we wash in the lake.

PARTICIPLE REVIEW

Find the participles in the following sentences:

1. The once-popular governor, criticized and defeated, gave his concession speech.

2. Having been summoned three times, the girl finally entered the room.

3. The brass handles, tarnished by the weather, became almost black.

4. The child, prattling in her crib, was happy and contented.

5. The referee, having been insulted by the player, ejected him from the game.

6. Her dance teacher, having encouraged Janet, was gratified when she won the scholarship.

7. Ricardo's arm, fractured when he fell, caused him great distress.

8. Having built a flourishing business, Mr. Chester needed a larger store.

9. The emergency warning signal having blared for one minute, we took shelter.

10. Junior, having sketched the street scene, planned to use it for a painting.

11. Having devised a trap for the escaped convict, the detective waited in his dark car.

12. The drug dealer's house and car having been confiscated, the state will receive all the money from their sale.

13. Stammering an embarrassed reply, the boy left the office.

14. Traffic, paralyzed by the accident, halted for an hour.

15. Sue, grumbling over her work, accidently dropped the tray of test tubes.

16. Calling for help, the driver slumped over the wheel.

17. The dog, being poked and prodded, finally bit his tormentors.

18. Mr. Slade, having been threatened by a drunken neighbor, called the police.

Make sentences using the participial forms of the following verbs.

1. screech	6. scrutinize	11. devote
2. wander	7. anticipate	12. murmur
3. plead	8. resemble	13. identify
4. sleep	9. reflect	14. accept
5. shovel	10. struggle	15. placate

GERUND

> A gerund is a verb form used as a noun.

The gerunds are underlined:

1. <u>Camping</u> is good fun.

2. Louise excelled at white water <u>kayaking</u>.

3. Mother enjoyed <u>having met</u> the mayor's wife.

4. His favorite sport is <u>swimming</u>.

5. Rover's <u>barking</u> annoyed the neighbor.

Find the gerunds:

1. Flying is a common way to travel.

2. Persisting is not always easy.

3. The law prohibits smoking in most public buildings.

4. Calling for help is our last hope.

5. His being sick postponed the trial.

6. My following the crowd was a great mistake.

7. The teacher disapproved of his being absent.

8. The crowd was thrilled at Masterson's pitching.

9. In hurrying home, she slipped on the ice.

10. The Hungarians considered migrating to northern Africa.

11. Shouting does no good.

12. Next Saturday ends the season for fishing.

13. Watering the garden is a regular chore.

14. The principal industry, making cotton cloth, engages the town's workers.

15. Paul enjoyed his new duty, answering the phone.

16. His laughing at the disappointed contestant seems out of place.

17. Maine has excellent soil for raising potatoes.

18. Have you noticed any change in her speaking?

19. We obliged the sick man by calling a doctor.

20. Formerly my hobby was mending old furniture.

21. Do you prefer swimming to sailing?

22. Politeness means acting in a considerate, courteous way.

23. Solving detective stories intrigues me.

24. Laying a brick walk is strenuous work.

25. Roberto told me of your winning the scholarship.

GERUND — SUBJECT OF A VERB

A gerund can be used as the subject of a verb.

The gerunds, subjects of the verb, are underlined:

1. Their <u>singing</u> was remarkably clear.
2. <u>Writing</u> compositions is not always easy.
3. His <u>carving</u> wooden ducks was very skillful.
4. <u>Guessing</u> a person's weight is often difficult.
5. <u>Running</u> a successful grocery store requires skill.

Find the gerunds that are subjects of a verb:

1. Working in a bank is an exacting job.
2. Her playing the radio annoyed the neighbors.
3. Harry's pitching won the baseball game.
4. Maria's swimming appears effortless.
5. Filing into the gymnasium took ten minutes.
6. Adjusting the carburetor is work for an expert.
7. Planting the seeds is only the first step in raising vegetables.
8. His coming at so late an hour exasperated his employer.
9. Working in the hot noonday sun is sometimes unwise.

10. Right after the accident, her trembling could not be stopped.

11. In this situation forceful speaking will be necessary to solve the problem.

12. Usually the harvesting of beans begins in June.

13. Building a model railroad requires skill and patience.

14. Digging wells is dangerous work.

15. Navigating a ship depends upon careful figuring.

16. Cleaning the old barn was a dusty job.

17. Exploring the cave under Constitution Hill was exciting.

18. Word processing with accuracy presupposes basic knowledge and lots of practice.

19. Separating the dogs was no job for a timid person.

20. Picnicking in the woods made a pleasant excursion.

21. Challenging that politician is an audacious act.

22. Making snowshoes is a demanding task.

23. Predicting the weather is a hazardous occupation.

24. Mending the sleeve was a moment's work.

25. Answering the telephone takes valuable time.

26. Buying gifts can be an enjoyable task.

27. Speaking several languages is a great asset.

GERUND — OBJECT OF A VERB

> A gerund can be used as object of a verb.

The gerunds, objects of the verb, are underlined:

1. I like <u>swimming</u> in salt water.
2. The pupils could not resist <u>talking</u> in class.
3. Courtesy demands <u>responding</u> to the invitation.
4. The girl studies <u>dancing</u> on Saturdays.
5. Father suggested <u>driving</u> to Boothbay Harbor for the day.

Find the gerunds that are objects of a verb:

1. The chef just finished frosting a cake.
2. Jack continued mumbling under his breath.
3. The child practiced casting his reel.
4. We enjoy picking apples in the autumn.
5. The angry worker demanded being paid on time.
6. The three teenagers admitted stealing the tapes.
7. I have often tried to understand playing chess.
8. The rascal acknowledged planting the stink bomb.
9. Dad suggested using the credit cards sparingly.

10. The rules forbid whistling in the library.

11. Did I mention seeing my friend?

12. Do your parents permit staying up until midnight?

13. The doctor recommended walking for an hour each day.

14. The chorus rehearsed singing for the show.

15. The sign urged diminishing speed on the wet pavement.

16. For years we have enjoyed visiting Lake George.

17. The school permits studying in the library.

18. The reporter described his having been ejected from the court.

19. Why do you hate touching snakes?

20. The weather bureau reported seeing a sharp drop in barometric pressure.

21. Some people enjoy bathing in cold water.

22. Mary despised Frank's telling lies.

23. The teacher suggested studying a little longer.

24. The players could not hear his calling the signals.

25. The state allows hunting deer in December.

GERUND — OBJECT OF A PREPOSITION

> A gerund may be used
> as object of a preposition.

The gerunds, used as objects of a preposition, are underlined:

1. My father knew about my <u>winning</u> first prize.

2. Nothing must interfere with your <u>studying</u>.

3. Billy is an expert at <u>identifying</u> birds.

4. The teacher began the contest by <u>dividing</u> the class into two groups.

5. Would you be satisfied merely with <u>seeing</u> a chocolate cake?

Find the gerunds used as objects of a preposition:

1. The runner was caught by his hesitating between bases.

2. Have you any interest in saving all that stuff?

3. Look on the box for directions for assembling the deck chair.

4. What are the problems in running a teen drop-in center?

5. Think before blurting out your answer.

6. The pilot managed to save the plane and passengers by using cool judgment.

7. We decided on a plan for exercising regularly.

8. The ten-minute break in class is for relaxing.

9. The athlete was not above boasting of his triumph.

10. We were accustomed to taking responsibility.

11. We were interested in exploring the city.

12. Rosalind was delighted at having been chosen leader.

13. The oil spill was in danger of floating down the coast.

14. The sick man despaired of regaining his former strength.

15. We read about starving children in many countries.

16. What can prevent those angry people from looting the stores?

17. We try to relax before eating dinner.

18. They arrived on time after rushing to get there.

19. In barking so much, the dog disturbed the neighbors.

20. I bought a cord of birch for burning in the fireplace.

GERUND — PREDICATE NOMINATIVE

> A gerund may be used
> as a predicate nominative.

The gerunds used as predicate nominatives are underlined:

1. The problem will be <u>locating</u> a campsite.
2. The difficulty is <u>paddling</u> against the wind.
3. The first step is <u>finding</u> a broom.
4. Her work was <u>helping</u> the poor find better jobs.
5. My profession is <u>practicing</u> law.

Find the gerunds used as predicate nominatives:

1. One joy of summer is going to the beach.
2. Connie's current interest is collecting and identifying shells.
3. My first task is mowing the lawn.
4. His sole diversion was reading detective stories.
5. Saving is not spending.
6. Tuning the motor is preparing for carefree driving.
7. A pleasant summer occupation is fishing off the wharf.
8. Her delight was learning to sing.
9. Our business in New England is catering to tourists.

10. The program for Saturday will be setting up the carnival.

11. Michael's chief duty was delivering the mail.

12. Good writing is more than inventing a lively tale.

13. Embezzling is stealing for one's own use.

14. A costly project is remodeling an old home.

15. Discretion is acting prudently.

16. One of her jobs was reminding her son to dress warmly.

17. Tonight's lesson will be memorizing four stanzas.

18. Lincoln's most memorable act was declaring slaves free.

19. His hardest task was changing the tire in a snowstorm.

20. Her assignment is making change in the lunchroom.

21. Sally's job will be greeting all visitors.

22. Your first thought should be checking the patient's pulse.

23. Jim's summer work has been selling ice cream and soda from the truck.

24. Our collegiate activity is singing in the chorus.

25. The last part of the program was the awarding of prizes.

GERUND REVIEW

Identify how the following gerunds are used:

1. Complaining about food is characteristic of children.

2. Mother proposed sending out the laundry.

3. The neighbors were upset by the dogs' fighting.

4. April means planting our vegetable garden.

5. Searching for the missing heir required several thousand dollars.

6. The pupil enjoyed doing original problems in geometry.

7. Her job was supervising the nurses in that department.

8. He bought dark glasses for protecting his eyes.

9. Harmonizing the disputed points was the judge's duty.

10. The company specialized in designing saws.

11. The noise I hear is an odd tapping at the window.

12. Carrying out the relief effort requires twelve planes.

13. The two boys were warned about fighting.

14. Having paralyzed transportation in the city was just one aspect of the blizzard.

15. Camping means swimming and sleeping out of doors.

16. Children always enjoy skating in winter.

17. The secret of chess is planning a good attack.

18. The doctor mentioned consulting with a heart specialist.

19. The difficulty of a foreign language is remembering new words.

20. Being praised is pleasant to most people.

21. The teacher suggested studying in the early evening.

22. This tool is useful for boring large holes.

23. Having been aroused at midnight frightened me.

24. The principal industry of Rockland is fishing.

25. She suffered a severe burn by lying in the hot sun.

26. Swinging too high caused the child to fall.

27. He had the reputation of paying all bills promptly.

28. Calling plays is the quarterback's job.

29. He learned to write by writing.

30. High honors means attaining A's in all subjects.

INFINITIVE — SUBJECT OF VERB

An infinitive is a verbal
usually preceded by to.

The infinitive used as subject of the verb is underlined:

1. To <u>diagram</u> this sentence is not difficult.

2. To <u>seize</u> an opportunity often demands courage.

3. To <u>have lighted</u> a match would have been disastrous.

4. To <u>reply</u> cautiously was the lawyer's advice.

5. To <u>collect</u> your mail for you while you are away is not a problem.

Find the infinitives used as subject of the verb:

1. To giggle seems characteristic of some children.

2. To climb a mountain appeals to many people.

3. To observe carefully presupposes sharp senses.

4. To apologize for the error was the proper action.

5. To examine the patient took an hour.

6. To have been warned should have been enough.

7. To be watching television so much cannot be good.

8. To beg for a bone was Tip's first trick.

9. To have ignored that traffic light was inexcusable.

10. To locate my glasses proved futile.

11. To have conceded defeat would have been difficult for him.

12. To be accused falsely angers any person.

13. To take any more time with this is impossible.

14. To be coaxed is sometimes annoying.

15. Always to be boasting disgusts one's friends.

Use each of these infinitives as subject of a verb.

1.	to detect	9.	to have answered
2.	to be studying	10.	to be plundered
3.	to have been finishing	11.	to be ready
4.	to be led	12.	to rescue
5.	to have been approached	13.	to be frightened
6.	to roam	14.	to have been seen
7.	to hesitate	15.	to employ
8.	to search	16.	to capture

INFINITIVE — OBJECT OF VERB

The infinitive used as object of a verb is underlined:

1. Jack intends <u>to earn</u> enough money to buy a car.

2. Roberta learned <u>to arrange</u> flowers.

3. The whole family decided <u>to go</u> on a picnic today.

4. I agreed <u>to pay</u> the dentist very soon.

5. The team determined <u>to win</u> the final game.

Find the infinitives — objects of the verb.

1. All of my family like to play softball.

2. The neighbors want to buy a cottage at Cape Cod.

3. I plan to travel by air.

4. Charles intended to visit St. Louis.

5. The clerk tried to locate the papers.

6. The artist decided to begin a new painting.

7. The man hoped to find work soon.

8. The diver vowed to locate the wreck.

9. My mother said to get out of bed.

10. Carmen wanted to finish her errands by noon.

11. The boy pretended to have a broken arm.

12. His father refused to lend him any money.

13. The lawyer began to question the witness.

14. Tomorrow I shall attempt to write the letter.

15. Tommy asked to be excused.

Use the following infinitives as objects of a transitive verb:

1.	to capture	9.	to submerge
2.	to manufacture	10.	to frown
3.	to rescue	11.	to watch
4.	to collapse	12.	to polish
5.	to stitch	13.	to navigate
6.	to explore	14.	to choose
7.	to pick	15.	to split
8.	to jump	16.	to flee

INFINITIVE — PREDICATE NOUN

The infinitive used as a predicate noun is underlined:

1. The quickest way to reach Santa Fe from Boston is <u>to fly</u>.

2. My first thought was <u>to bandage</u> my foot.

3. His assignment had been <u>to interview</u> the governor.

4. Her hardest job is <u>to write</u> neatly.

5. The teacher seemed <u>to understand</u> the reason.

Find the infinitives used as predicate nouns:

1. The duty of the foreman is to keep workers busy.

2. The tendency of some people is to blame others.

3. The pastime of many teenagers is to listen to music.

4. The student's hope was to spend spring vacation at home.

5. Elena's plan had been to save for college.

6. The jet planes seemed to collide in the air.

7. Patrice's aim was to practice medicine.

8. The company's policy was to hire people without discriminating.

9. Tonight the weather seemed to turn much colder.

10. The purpose of carpooling is to conserve energy.

11. My next task is to paint the bookcase.

12. One reason she worked was to send her daughter to college.

13. This morning our first task is to sort through these papers.

14. The girl's visit to the library was to find a particular book.

15. Our intention has been to inform all the parents of this meeting.

16. The only answer of the boy was to stammer an excuse.

17. A shot from a revolver is to start the relay race.

18. The arrival of the circus seemed to excite all the children.

19. Denmark Versey's objective was to organize the slaves.

20. The purpose of the tall chimney was to provide a strong draft.

FORMS OF THE INFINITIVE

> An infinitive has tense: present and perfect;
> An infinitive has voice: active and passive.

present active   :   to call

perfect active   :   to have called

present passive   :   to be called

perfect passive   :   to have been called

Find the infinitive in each sentence, and give the tense and voice:

1.   Your friend has gone to buy some groceries.

2.   The house seemed to have fallen into ruins.

3.   The defendant asked to be examined again.

4.   To have been promoted would be what you deserve.

5.   To have replied courteously should not have been too difficult.

6.   I like to go visit my uncle who trains horses.

7.   Walter was disappointed not have been chosen captain of the team.

8.   To do the work as well as you can is best.

9.   The children ought to have avoided the alley.

10.   The photographer expects to be paid at once.

11. To be ridiculed is not pleasant.

12. The police wanted to question the store owner.

13. Tom hated to be asked for money.

14. The spell of dry weather appears to have been ended.

15. His ambition had been to learn journalism.

16. The traveler appeared to have lost his luggage.

17. John offered to rescue the cat in the tree.

18. The garden ought to have been watered every night.

19. How pleasant it is to have visited Washington!

20. The ribbon on the typewriter needs to be changed.

21. Tim hoped to be hired for the summer.

22. To repair the fuel pump wasted two hours.

23. It is gratifying to have been awarded first prize.

24. The transatlantic flight was to have left at midnight.

25. To have been consulted would have pleased Ada.

26. Paul's ambition was to have a driver's license.

27. The unprepared student was anxious not to be called.

INFINITIVE REVIEW

Identify how the following infinitives are used:

1. To have plunged into the cold stream would have been fatal.

2. Do you wish to buy my bicycle?

3. The best plan is to consult the doctor.

4. The air appears to be much warmer.

5. The businessman hopes to travel to San Francisco.

6. To be successful requires steady work.

7. To have been wrongly accused was not pleasant.

8. My mother promised to send me to camp next summer.

9. Why don't you try to understand the problems?

10. Her current work is to go over all of the records.

11. John seems to be late again today.

12. To see that everyone is fed is a big responsibility.

13. The traffic was forced to detour.

14. These directions are to be followed during fire drills.

15. The motorist tried to change the tire.

16. The patient seems to have improved overnight.

17. To have met the novelist was a great experience.

18. To be paid on time is the worker's right.

19. His favorite relaxation was to work in his garden.

20. The girl hoped to finish writing her paper by noon.

21. The plow is to clear the snow this afternoon.

22. To have been overlooked would have been disappointing.

23. I hesitate to loan you my new car.

24. Timmy begged to go skiing.

25. Their only hope was to reach the house where lights still burned.

26. That agency is to provide the food and blankets.

27. I will be able to attend the party.

28. His only hope was to plead for more time.

29. To have been accepted in the art show was a great honor.

30. The meeting is to begin promptly at six o'clock.

31. To have struggled would have been useless.

32. To devote their lives to helping others is what they chose.

NOUN CLAUSE

> A noun clause is a subordinate clause used as a noun.
> A noun clause may be used as subject, object of a verb,
> object of a preposition, or predicate nominative.

The noun clauses are underlined:

a. As subject of a sentence:

    1. That the winter will be severe is the meteorologist's prediction.

    2. That Barry could speak Italian quite surprised me.

b. As object of a verb:

    1. I perceived that I was lost in New York.

    2. Tom understood that he had won the scholarship.

c. As object of a preposition:

    1. Give this book to whoever needs one.

    2. These seats are reserved for whatever musicians appear.

d. As predicate nominative:

    1. Betsy's wish is that she be promoted.

    2. The truth is that you failed in three tests.

Find the noun clauses. Tell how each is used.

1. Whoever finishes the examples may go to the library.

2. Sally learned that she was promoted to partner.

3. Hand this water to whichever runner comes first.

4. My guess is that it will rain before morning.

5. That air travel can be dangerous is clear.

6. The danger of these rapids is that the canoe may capsize.

7. The storekeeper asked what I wanted.

8. The old man asked only for what was owed him.

9. Sharon knows that we depend upon her.

10. The maxim that whoever works succeeds does not always prove true.

11. Informing and educating is what we must do.

12. Our dog barks at whoever walks by on the street.

13. Pack your lunch in whatever bag you have.

14. A neighbor discovered that our dog had gotten away.

15. The plan is that we meet you at the airport.

16. That all the roads will be plowed today seems probable.

17. Whoever has something to say will be heard.

18. The commuter will take whichever train comes first.

19. Wait here for what you ordered.

20. That people are generous should not surprise you.

21. The messenger felt that he was being shadowed.

ADJECTIVE CLAUSE

An adjective clause is a
subordinate clause used as an adjective.

The adjective clauses are underlined:

1. Give the dollar to the person <u>who dropped it</u>.

2. People <u>who have red hair</u> are said to have excitable dispositions.

3. The barn <u>that burned</u> belonged to my grandfather.

4. I see the solution to the problem <u>that baffled me</u>.

5. Ted visited the neighbor <u>who had broken his leg</u>.

Find the adjective clauses:

1. Mother bought a clock that chimes every fifteen minutes.

2. The canoe paddle that Hal made is broken.

3. June writes stories that make me laugh.

4. We enjoyed being with children who use their imagination.

5. One o'clock is the hour when the school is dismissed.

6. This is the spot where the trucks collided.

7. Bob is the boy whom I like best.

8. The magician who entertained the school is my friend's uncle.

9. Here is the key that was lost.

10. Maurice Sendak has illustrated many books that appeal to children.

11. The section of the zoo that opened last weekend has two elephants.

12. A mail carrier counted the deliveries that had been made.

13. The welder who fell from the scaffolding was seriously hurt.

14. Storms that arise in the south are often violent.

15. She searched for the boot that was misplaced in the closet.

16. The judge pondered the remark that the lawyer had made.

17. The airplane that just landed has a faulty propeller.

18. The swimming pool, which was our only place to cool off, was closed for repairs.

19. The book that she recommended is not available.

20. Appliances that dry clothes are useful machines.

21. Hand me the paper that I dropped.

22. Send for the boy who made that accusation.

23. The gray clouds that suddenly filled the sky seemed ominous.

ADVERBIAL CLAUSE

An adverbial clause is a
subordinate clause used as an adverb.

The adverbial clauses are underlined:

1. The singer smiled <u>when he faced the crowd</u>.

2. Let everyone read <u>until the bell rings</u>.

3. The mail carrier has been cautious <u>since he was bitten</u> by the dog.

4. The driver slammed on her brakes <u>as soon as she saw the deer</u>.

5. <u>When they aren't so worried</u>, my co-workers are more fun to be with.

Find the adverbial clauses:

1. Since the rains have come, the drought is broken.

2. When Sara arrived home from the pound, she had a dog with her.

3. While Tom and Stephanie set up the tent, Derek and Margot gathered the wood.

4. Charlie is liable to know little unless he studies every night.

5. The wind often dies down when the sun sets.

6. The players shook hands after the game was over.

7. Until the whistle blew the substitute could not enter the game.

8. When we reached Buffalo, New York, we looked for a motel.

9. As soon as the victim recovered, he sued the drunken driver.

10. The homeowner was shocked when she learned the new tax rate.

11. While the bicyclists were looking for shelter, the storm broke upon them.

12. When foreigners first see New York, they are amazed by its size.

13. As soon as the busybody heard the news, he told all the neighbors.

14. As I climbed the hill, I wondered how far I could see from the top.

15. After Gretchen washed and waxed the car, she went for a ride.

16. He ate a sandwich while he talked to a client.

17. When I opened the curtain, I saw a brilliant sunrise.

18. While Ted's job lasted, he had a good time.

19. Call me as soon as the doctor arrives.

20. After Pat finished her homework, she went for a stroll.

21. Mind the baby until its mother returns.

22. When you read an article, concentrate on what point the author is making.

CLAUSE REVIEW

Find the clauses in the following sentences, and tell how each is used:

1. The frost, which was severe, transmuted green leaves to red and yellow.

2. The crowd shrieked with joy when the fullback intercepted the ball.

3. That they should try to fly in such a storm seems unnecessarily foolish.

4. The money that my parents put aside during my childhood is for my college education.

5. The birdwatchers noticed that the nest had several eggs in it.

6. While we worked to meet the deadline, we took no phone calls.

7. Until we signed the lease, we could not believe the apartment was ours.

8. The prize is for whoever earns it.

9. Her income, which I calculate at fifty thousand dollars a year, has not always been so large.

10. Her one ambition is that she succeed as an architect.

11. When he worked at the computer, he lost all sense of time.

12. The room that we entered was so dark we could see nothing.

13. That the boy was lying was more than evident.

14. The silversmith, who was burnishing a bowl, took great pains with his work.

15. Unless I persuade my mother, I cannot go out.

16. Whoever knows the answer may write it on the blackboard.

17. If this rain doesn't stop, we can't go on our bicycle trip.

18. Must you follow every idea that occurs to you?

19. Tom, whose red face appeared in the window, waved to his friend.

20. That his money would soon be gone appeared evident to the boy.

21. When John is perplexed, a deep frown creases his forehead.

22. As soon as the tow truck had cleared the accident, the traffic began to move.

23. The sunset, which tinges the clouds in salmon and purple, will soon fade.

24. Send the projector to whatever teacher asks for it.

25. That there will be skating tomorrow seems certain.

1. The photograph, which shows a thin, frightened girl, is from her childhood.

2. To find answers to your questions is his job.

3. Solving travelers' problems often taxes the information-desk operator.

4. That the restaurant would be closed after our long drive seemed too much bad luck.

5. Neither verbal directions nor an obscure map helped us find the address we sought.

6. The defense contractor, whose work was confidential, remained in seclusion.

7. Having seen the dark, funnel-shaped clouds, I headed for the basement.

8. The amiable companions decided to attend the concert together.

9. Why do teachers require my studying irksome lessons every night?

10. The frugal meal that he ate seemed to satisfy him.

11. The lawyer professes to give every client her best advice.

12. The burned-out car which we just passed seemed ominous.

13. Having talked incessantly, the man finally gave me a chance to comment.

14. Either the new bond issue will pass or it will fail.

15. A person who disdains courtesy and consideration toward others may live to regret this attitude.

16. The man showed great forbearance in not punishing the dog.

17. When the eclipse occurred, an unusual light overspread our town.

18. Having been a diligent student, Anne won the scholarship.

19. The blossoming spring trees spread their pollen.

20. My eyes watered severely but only in May.

21. The child, whose involuntary shriek pierced the air, was plucked from the water.

22. That you will comprehend today's lesson remains to be seen.

23. To glide over the high bar without touching it is the aim.

24. The gravity of the accident being apparent, the police summoned an ambulance.

25. The sign of measles is the red, blotching skin.

26. People who are garrulous are seldom silent.

27. The scientist contrived a rocket that can rise hundreds of miles.

28. Neither the heavy luggage nor the late flight departure could dampen her enthusiasm for the trip to Amsterdam.

29. When the pain stopped, the patient uttered a sigh of relief.

30. The storm appears to have diminished in the last hour.

31. That your careful work has been noticed is true.

32. The day which dawned was clear and serene.

33. Being responsible for the children, I watched them carefully at the pool.

34. His finding the two-hundred-year-old document caused great interest among scholars.

35. One duty of a president is to look out for the welfare of all the citizens.

36. Filled with contempt, the woman spoke rapidly.

37. Having no warm jacket, I felt the cold penetrate my body.

38. The saxophonist who plays so melodiously is only twenty years old.

39. To tell lies is not only deceitful but also destroys trust.

40. The man whom I waited for two hours to see proved to be inaccessible.

41. Having worked all summer on our garden plot, we enjoyed the vegetables and flowers we had grown.

42. To recognize one's failures is to have hope of correcting them.

43. The inventor succeeded in originating a transparent metal.

44. The emotional scene in which the mother pleaded for her imprisoned son was the saddest of all.

45. Fortunate is the person who has good health and close friends.

46. Being filled with excitement, George rushed to the door.

47. When the movie was over, we sat quietly in our seats.

48. The sound of the jet taking off reverberated through the neighborhood.

49. Mark tried to imitate the dexterous juggler.

50. The boy, whose impertinence provoked the teacher, remained after school.

51. That the bull's anger would subside was his only hope of getting out of the field.

52. Inundated by frequent showers, the river almost flooded its banks.

53. This newborn infant is most certainly strong.

54. A hard job is tapering the legs of the chair.

55. We all attended her birthday celebration, a large catered dinner.

56. The family's plan was to visit the Grand Canyon.

57. Having been warned of the dangerous chemicals, the community took action to stop their use.

58. The blow that caused the man to writhe injured his leg.

59. The police, when the mother called, began the search for her missing child.

60. An elephant is too ponderous to move any faster.

61. At the season's first concert, the chorus sang most admirably.

62. When the taxi honked, they grabbed their bags and ran to the car.

63. The dancers moved with the greatest harmony.

64. The shrill firebell echoing through the school, the students and teachers moved out quickly to the driveway.

65. What a good companion is the person who possesses a sense of humor.

66. Friends, let's eat.

67. Her speaking so determinedly made them proud.

68. A soft smile flooded his face.

69. That pneumonia is often fatal is unfortunately true.

70. To lie sunning oneself should be done with caution.

71. Who allows you to tease that poor dog?

72. That man whose voice you hear is an editor of the local paper.

73. Neither coaxing nor promises could affect the screaming child.

74. Laughing at my inept try, Tim seized the rope and tossed it neatly around the post on the dock.

75. The pedestrian noticed his having come to a stop.

76. "I hope to answer all your questions," said the guide, leading us into the old house.

77. The surf which pounded the beach so tumultuously could be heard far inland.

78. Teach your children to love reading.

79. What dreadful news has made Bettina so sad?

80. Exhorted by the cheering spectators, the lead runner pulled away from those nearby.

81. Having been capsized by a gigantic wave, the trawler sank.

82. The teacher whom she admired so much always treated her fairly.

83. Charles was scolded for associating with such odious boys.

84. The bewilderment on Malcolm's face revealed how he felt.

85. When he sought to catch the squirrel, he made an ingenious trap.

86. To continue driving in this heavy fog is dangerous.

87. Can Mary or Caroline replicate this intricate design?

88. Malice having filled his heart, the thief even robbed the only person who had helped him.

89. The problem was to tint the fabric a soft yellow.

90. Jennifer Barrett, a shrewd lawyer, succeeded in freeing her client.

INDEX